UNDERSTANDING
DIGITAL COMPUTERS

UNDERSTANDING

DIGITAL COMPUTERS

RONALD BENREY

JOHN F. RIDER PUBLISHER, INC., NEW YORK

a division of HAYDEN PUBLISHING COMPANY, INC.

Preface

This book has been written for the person who wants to develop an understanding of digital computers and their operation without trudging through an excess of design and construction detail. The author feels that this volume will bridge the wide gap that exists between complete digital computer textbooks and elementary picture books. It is a book for the person who wants more than a "cocktail party conversation" familiarity with digital computers, but who does not have the background or the desire to delve into a rigorous consideration of electronic digital computer design techniques.

A digital computer is a "system" designed and built to do a specific job. This book discusses computers in terms of the similar, and simple, building blocks that make up the system. The function of these building blocks is stressed, rather than their actual electronic construction, for although future digital computers will undoubtedly have building blocks fabricated of totally new electronic components, the function of the building blocks will remain the same.

As an analogy, consider the automobile — a system designed for ground transportation. Anyone who wishes to learn about automobiles would probably begin by considering the functions of the building blocks of the automobile system: the engine, the body, the chassis, the wheels, etc.

All automobiles have an engine. It may be air-cooled or water-cooled, two-cycle or four-cycle, front- or rear-mounted. In any case, the engine in every automobile performs the same function. Body, chassis, and wheel design and construction may also vary from automobile to automobile, but these building blocks, too, always perform the same function.

What is true about automobiles is valid for digital computers. The most important step in learning about them is the mastery of an understanding of the functions of their basic building blocks.

In this book, the author has selected a group of topics that he considers to be the starting points for a study of digital computers and computation and has arranged them in a coherent and connected order:

Chapter 1 is a brief introduction to digital computation. It presents a short history of computers and defines the basic functional units.

Chapter 2 is an introduction to programming. Only after we know what a digital computer is expected to do can we begin to think about design.

v

Chapter 3 discusses the binary number system (and number systems in general), binary arithmetic, and the reasons why binary numbers are used in a computer.

Chapter 4 presents a simplified introduction to logical design techniques, including Boolean algebra. The basic building blocks are described, and a few comprehensive examples illustrate how they can be combined to build circuits that will perform binary arithmetic.

Chapter 5 describes the actual electronic circuitry of the building blocks, including a brief description of the switching properties of diodes, vacuum tubes, and transistors.

Chapter 6 combines the results of Chapters 3 and 4 to show how electronic circuitry performs arithmetic.

Chapter 7 discusses the control circuitry of a digital computer.

Chapter 8 is a brief survey of storage devices and techniques.

Chapter 5 can be by-passed by readers with no electronics background. It isn't necessary to understand the electronic circuitry of the building blocks in order to understand their function in a computer.

The reader is urged to consult the glossary whenever a definition or name becomes a bit hazy.

New York
November 1963   RONALD BENREY

Contents

1—Introduction

A computer is a machine that handles numbers. As shown in Fig. 1-1, *input numbers* are fed into the computer, and *output numbers* are taken out. The computer *operates* on the input numbers to produce the output numbers. Input numbers might be numerical values associated with an arithmetic problem. In this case, the computer would solve the problem, and the output numbers will be the answer. Or, the input numbers might be raw data of some kind, which the computer will *process*. In this case, the output numbers will present the input data in a more understandable or convenient form.

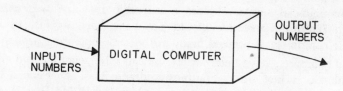

FIG. 1-1.   A digital computer operates on numbers.

Electronic automatic digital computers are the newest link in a chain of calculating machines that traces its beginnings back to the abacus. Primitive man had no need for calculating machines. His ten fingers helped him to count his possessions, which was essentially the only arithmetic he did. Eventually, though, numbers were used to represent larger and larger quantities, and arithmetic grew to include addition, subtraction, multiplication and division. Fingers soon became inadequate as an aid to calculation.

The abacus was developed in the Far East about 600 B.C., probably as an aid to accountants involved in trade and commerce, and is still used today

1

in many parts of the world. A skilled operator can perform arithmetic on an abacus faster than a worker using a mechanical desk calculating machine, although it takes a lot of practice to be able to multiply and divide quickly on the abacus. The abacus is considered to be the forerunner of the modern digital computer because it relies on a counting process in order to calculate.

The first mechanical adding machine was built in 1642 by the French philosopher Blaise Pascal. Pascal's machine used notched wheels to represent numbers. The wheels were geared together so that turning one wheel ten notches shifted the next wheel forward one notch. Multiplication could be performed by repeatedly adding the same number together to form a product; division, by repeated subtraction. This same basic principle is used today in odometers (automobile mileage meters), cash registers, and hundreds of other counting mechanisms.

Gottfried Wilhelm von Leibnitz, a German philosopher and mathematician, developed an adding machine called the "stepped reckoner" in the years between 1671 and 1694. It was based on Pascal's machine, but it contained an additional gearing arrangement that enabled it to multiply directly. Modern desk calculating machines are direct descendants of Leibnitz's stepped reckoner.

Both Pascal's and Leibnitz's machines were manually operated; a human operator had to feed the numbers in individually for each operation. In 1812, Charles Babbage, an English inventor, devised an *automatic* mechanical computer. His plans called for a machine that could follow instructions and solve problems automatically. Unfortunately, the British government withdrew financial support before a full-scale machine was completed. Although Babbage's machine would not have been as fast as modern electronic computers, it utilized many of the same operating principles.

Digital computers have been widely used to solve scientific and engineering problems. In fact, the computing requirements of the Federal Government and the aircraft industry, prior to and during World War II, sparked the development of modern high-speed computers. Soon after the war computers were being used to solve equations applicable to problems in nuclear physics. More recently, computers have become data processing machines, and perform routine clerical work as well as aid in high-level decision making in business.

Advances in electronic digital computer technology have made possible many spectacular scientific achievements that would have seemed like "science fiction" three or four decades ago. Names of many computers have become household terms, and the newspapers are forever reporting the latest feat performed by an "electronic brain." As a result, amazing intellectual powers and super-human thinking abilities have been attributed to digital computers, and they are generally pictured as incredibly complex electronic machines, aglow with flashing lights.

It's certainly true that digital computers can perform the lengthy mathematical calculations that go along with scientific research. It's also true that computers have revolutionized such fields as data processing and industrial control. However, digital computers can not "think," and, as we shall see, they are not as complicated as most people believe. In fact, computers owe·many of their capabilities to their inherent simplicity.

WHAT IS A DIGITAL COMPUTER?

A digital computer is a device that can perform arithmetic operations and make simple *logical decisions* according to *instructions* it has been given. The arithmetic operations include addition, subtraction, multiplication and division. A typical logical decision might be to compare the size of two numbers, and indicate which of the two is larger. (We will discuss logic and its applications in a later chapter.)

The computer performs these operations at a tremendous rate of speed because it is built of electronic components and operates automatically. No human control is necessary when the computer is running. The human operator of a mechanical desk calculator must feed numbers into the machine and select the proper arithmetic operation at the start of every calculation. An automatic digital computer, on the other hand, performs a long sequence of individual calculations by automatically following a set of step-by-step instructions called a *program*. Once this program has been "written" and fed into the computer by its human operators, the computer controls itself.

No computer "thinks for itself"; it only operates at high speed according to the instructions it has received. If there is an error in the program (if the computer has been incorrectly instructed), the decision the computer supplies will be in error. By the same token, if it is fed correct instructions a computer is capable of unchallenged accuracy. Present digital computers can perform thousands of consecutive calculations without making a single error.

Programs of instructions have been written to solve all sorts of scientific and engineering problems, as well as data processing operations involving hundreds of thousands of similar calculations. Although a single program may take a team of trained "programmers" several months to write, a computer may run through it in a few minutes.

It may seem hard to believe that a machine capable of performing only addition, subtraction, multiplication and division can solve the complex scientific and engineering problems that we usually classify as "higher mathematics." Actually, a good part of higher mathematics was developed as a shortcut to solve such problems. Many advanced problems can be broken down into combinations of the basic arithmetic operations. This simplification of processes, however, enormously increases the number of simple operations involved. Differential equations, for example, can often be reduced to a form that can be solved, approximately, by large numbers of simple calculations. Adding up several thousand of the terms in an "infinite power series" is an easy way (for a digital computer!) to find the value of a trigonometric function.

There are many scientific problems that can't be solved by the methods used in higher mathematics. A typical example is the set of "simultaneous linear equations" that an electrical engineer sometimes writes after studying a complicated circuit. Sets of over twenty-five equations are not unusual. Solving these equations with the help of a slide rule or desk calculator is a long, tedious process. A digital computer can produce a solution in a few minutes, as all its calculations involve "simple arithmetic."

Calculating the orbit of an earth satellite can require the solution of hundreds of thousands of individual simple arithmetic problems. Any school boy could do the arithmetic, but he would be an old scholar before he was even close to the final answer. Fortunately for our "Man in Space" effort, high speed digital computers can work this problem in a few hours or even minutes.

At the same time that mathematicians are looking for new short cuts to solve advanced problems, computer programmers are searching for new ways to break down the same problems into sequences of simple arithmetic operations.

WHAT DOES "DIGITAL" MEAN?

The "digital" in digital computer tells us a lot about how these devices calculate. As we have said, input numbers are fed into a digital computer and output numbers are taken out. But what happens inside?

"Digital" describes *any* calculating mechanism that represents quantity with integers as it calculates. Another way of saying the same thing is that a digital computer solves a problem by actually doing arithmetic, in much the same way a person would "by hand."

If you were to look inside a digital computer as it is performing a calculation (we will in later chapters), you would see different numbers represented by the mechanism at various times: At the start of the problem, the input numbers would be visible. Then, as the calculation goes on, "intermediate" results would appear. Finally, the answer would pop into view, just before it is sent out through the output. In effect, the computer is "writing the numbers down" as it does the arithmetic.

Notice that "digital" can be used to describe any calculating device that represents quantity in this fashion. Desk calculators, cash registers, abaci and most mechanical counters, such as odometers, meet this requirement. These devices are actually mechanical digital computers. The abacus represents numbers with wooden beads, the others use gears or notched wheels.

ANALOG VERSUS DIGITAL

The rapidly growing science of automatic electronic computer technology includes two completely different categories of computers: digital computers and *analog* computers. Although this book is concerned exclusively with digital machines, it is certainly necessary to briefly consider analog computers.

As has been said, digital computers work with numbers composed of discrete integers, and calculate in much the same way as a person doing arithmetic by hand. Analog computers solve problems by establishing some physical *analogy* between the computer system and the system being studied. Every input variable is represented by some measurable physical quantity.

A slide rule is a simple mechanical analog computer. Distances along the various scales represent the numbers that are being manipulated. The final answer is read as an "answer distance" on the appropriate scale.

Electronic analog computers represent the input variables with electric currents and voltages. In effect, a problem is solved by reproducing it with electronic components. The problem equations are represented in the computer by electronic circuits whose equations are of the same form as the problem equations. Answers are found by measuring appropriate currents or voltages in the circuit.

Analog computers are very useful for solving complicated equations having several continuously varying input variables. Generally, they are simpler and less expensive than digital computers, but are not as accurate or as flexible. Nevertheless, a sizeable fraction of the automatic computers that exist today are of the analog variety.

THE BLACK BOX COMPUTER

If you have ever tried to teach simple "short" division to a young child, you know that it can be an exasperating experience. You probably consider the problem and its solution to be "easy" or "crystal clear," and yet your pupil just can't grasp it. The difficulty here, however, is not the child's intelligence, it is your own sophistication. The four basic arithmetic operations (addition, subtraction, multiplication and division) are so familiar to us, and we use them so often in our daily lives, that they have almost become second nature. The clerk in the grocery store, for example, is concerned only with the mechanics involved in adding a column of numbers, not with the theory behind addition.

Can you prove mathematically that $1 + 1$ equals 2. The "proof" is actually quite complicated, yet you have no difficulty determining the proper answer because of your long experience with numbers. Your young pupil, however, has not had any experience in working with numbers. Numbers and their manipulation are still new ideas. He must be taught the meaning of each operation.

In many ways, the "mind" of an electronic digital computer is like the untrained mind of a child; it, too, must be instructed clearly and carefully in the mechanics involved in every step needed to arrive at the proper solution of a problem. The major differences, though, are that the computer will not learn from experience, and that it is "taught" with a program of instructions.

The majority of people who use digital computers — statisticians, businessmen, mathematicians, and so on — probably have little or no idea of what is going on in the innards of their machine. There is no harm in this. It is perfectly permissible to treat the computer as a "black box" into which a programmer feeds instructions and problem numbers, and which quickly produces a set of numerical answers. Just as a good driver doesn't have to understand the operation of a gasoline engine, detailed knowledge of computer circuitry isn't necessary to operate a computer. This approach will work as long as you remember the type of "mind" you are dealing with. The black box is a choosy fellow, and feeding it any old instruction will not do.

An essential quality demanded of the computer operator, therefore, is that he be able to set up a program that will guide the computer in an orderly step-by-step manner from the start of the problem to its finish. Obviously, the black box must not be asked to do anything it isn't capable of doing, which means that only the simple arithmetic operations are allowed. Finally, each guiding instruction can contain only one operation.

All this brings us back to a point mentioned earlier: problems are broken down into a sequence of simple arithmetic operations before they are given to a computer. This breaking-down process is often considered a part of writing the program for the problem. Because the idea of a "sequence of simple arithmetic operations" is vital to understanding digital computation, we will discuss it before we look into the black box.

Consider the following simple problem:

$$8x + \frac{7y}{3} - 4z = D$$

Given: $x = 2, \ y = 6, \ z = 1$

Find: D

This type of "plug-in" problem is certainly familiar to anyone who has studied algebra. It's almost easy enough to do mentally, without pencil and paper. For the sake of illustration, though, let's go through the problem step by step.

Notice that the equation, $8x + \dfrac{7y}{3} - 4z = D$, is actually a "shorthand" way of writing the following instructions:

Step	Instruction	Result
1.	Multiply the given value of x (which is 2) by 8	$8x = 8 \cdot 2 = 16$
2.	Multiply the given value of y (which is 6) by 7	$7y = 7 \cdot 6 = 42$
3.	Divide the result of Step 2 by 3	$\dfrac{42}{3} = 14$
4.	Add the results of Steps 1 and 3	$\begin{array}{rl} 16 & \text{(from Step 1)} \\ + \ 14 & \text{(from Step 3)} \\ \hline 30 & \end{array}$
5.	Multiply the given value of z (which is 1) by 4	$4z = 4 \cdot 1 = 4$
6.	Subtract the result of Step 5 from the result of Step 4	$\begin{array}{rl} 30 & \text{(from Step 4)} \\ - \ \ 4 & \text{(from Step 5)} \\ \hline 26 & \text{final answer} \end{array}$

$$D = 26$$

Solving this simple problem required a total of three separate multiplications, one division, one addition and one subtraction. We arrived at the answer, $D = 26$, by following an orderly sequence of simple arithmetic steps. This sequence illustrates only one of the many possible ways the problem could have been solved. There aren't any hard and fast rules stating which multiplication to do first, or whether to perform the addition before the subtraction. These arbitrary decisions rest with the judgment of the person solving the problem.

Usually, we don't look at arithmetic in terms of separate steps. Experience enables us to take short-cuts, combining two or more steps together without giving it any thought. However, the problems solved by a digital computer are many times more complex than those we're used to and the computer cannot be arbitrary or rely on past experience; a more orderly and systematic approach is necessary.

An often-used aid for determining a correct sequence of simple arithmetic operations is the *flow diagram*. This is simply a pictorial representation of the various steps in a problem. A flow diagram for the preceding equation, $8x + \dfrac{7y}{3} - 4z = D$, is illustrated in Fig. 1-2. Notice that the individual operations follow the direction of the arrowheads. Fig. 1-3 shows a flow diagram for a more complicated equation: $y = ax^2 + b$.

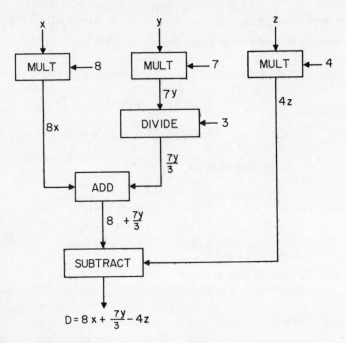

FIG. 1-2.   Flow diagram for solution of $D = 8x + \dfrac{7y}{3} - 4z$.

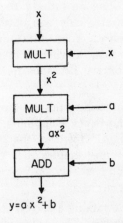

FIG. 1-3.   Flow diagram for solution of $y = ax^2 + b$.

INSIDE THE BLACK BOX

Big or little, fast or not so fast, all digital computers are organized along similar lines. Every digital computer is made up of five *functional units* that work together in close harmony: the Input section; the Output section; the Arithmetic section; the Control section; and the Memory section.

The *input section* is essentially a communications device through which problem numbers and instructions are fed into the machine. Every digital computer has its own "language," and part of the programmer's job is to convert the problem numbers and instructions into a form that the computer can understand and work with.

Someday, digital computers may be able to read handwritten instructions directly from a piece of paper. Today, however, *punched cards, perforated paper tape* and *magnetic tape* are typically used to "talk" to a computer. Data and instructions are *punched* in the paper tape or cards according to a code. The input section "reads" the information they contain, and passes it on to the appropriate section.

The term "information" refers to both instructions and problem data. All five functional units are digital mechanisms. Therefore, all information flowing within a computer, including problem numbers and instructions, must be in numerical form. For this purpose, a full vocabulary of computer language based on a numerical "alphabet" has been written.

The *output section* is another communications device, whose function is to display the results of the calculations taking place inside the computer. Final answers alone may be displayed, or the output section may present the detailed results of each step in a problem solution.

The output section translates information from machine language back to a more familiar form. Typical output devices include high-speed printers, electric typewriters, punched cards, magnetic tape and, occasionally, cathode-ray tubes.

The *arithmetic section* is the actual calculating mechanism which performs the arithmetic operations, called for by the instructions. The arithmetic section is the functional core of a digital computer; the other four sections oversee its operation and control the flow of problem numbers into it and results out of it.

The arithmetic section is often compared to a desk calculating machine, since numbers are fed into it before it is directed to perform an arithmetic operation.

The *control section* directs the overall functioning of the computer according to the program of instructions. In effect, the control section executes the programmer's orders by *decoding* the instructions and then generating electrical signals which tell the other sections what to do.

Although control is considered a single function, the circuits of the control section are spread throughout a computer. In many computers it is possible to point out the other four sections — to say, "this chassis houses the arithmetic section," or, "that unit is the output section." Control circuitry, however, is found almost everywhere, channeling the flow of information, carrying out the instructions, checking the results of each step for error and otherwise operating the different sections at the right time.

If the arithmetic section is compared to a calculating machine, the control secton is analogous to the mind of its human operator.

The *memory section* is a "storage depot" where instructions and problem numbers are kept until needed by the control and arithmetic sections. Automatic operation requires that the computer have on hand all of the instructions and problem numbers necessary to solve a problem before it begins to work out the solution. At the start of a problem solution, the programmer stores this information in the memory section by feeding it into the input section.

During each individual step of the solution the memory is used to remember the intermediate results. You'll recall that the simple algebra problem illustrated earlier contained six steps, and that the results of some of the steps were not used immediately. For example, the sixth step consisted of subtracting the result of step 5 from the result of step 4. The results of each step are called *intermediate results*. If this equation was solved on a digital computer using this sequence of operations, the result of step 4 would be placed in the memory section until called for.

The memory section is divided into many individual *cells*, each capable of storing one piece of information — a problem number, an intermediate result or an instruction. Each cell is identified by its own *address*, or location, in the memory section. The control section can put information into or take information out of any specified memory location, if it knows the address.

A good way to picture the memory section is to think of a room full of filing cabinets. Each file drawer can be located rapidly because each has its own number, and all the drawers have equal capacity. Every memory cell is analogous to one of the file drawers.

One of the most important characteristics of a memory section is its *access time*, which is the time required to put information into or take information out of any memory location. A small access time means that the problem solution will not be interrupted each time a new piece of information is called for. This is essential to high-speed computation.

Actually, the memory section of most computers contains more than one kind of memory device. We will discuss a few of them in detail in Chapter 8. The memory used to store instructions must have a large capacity so that long programs can be accommodated; but it only has to "read out" one instruction at a time. A magnetic tape memory, "kissing cousin" to the home tape recorder, is often used to store instructions.

In most scientific applications, the memory that will store intermediate results, on the other hand, doesn't need as large a capacity, since the same memory space can be used over and over again. After an intermediate result has been used, it can be discarded to make room for new results. However, it must have a very short access time so that little time is lost as intermediate results are transferred back and forth.

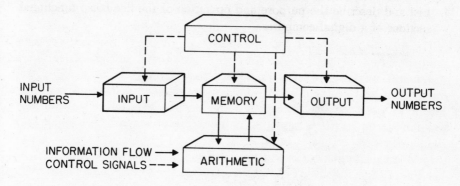

FIG. 1-4.   The five functional units of a digital computer.

This five functional unit representation of a digital computer provides a good model of a real machine. Although minor details may vary among different computers, the solution of a problem involves the units in the following steps:

1. The programmer breaks the problem down into a form that can be solved by a sequence of simple arithmetic operations and writes the program.

2. The program of instructions (including the problem numbers) is fed into the input section. The information is placed in appropriate memory section locations.

3. If the instructions are correct (if they are in proper form), the control section takes over and processes the problem numbers according to the instructions. Throughout the calculation there is a flow of information between the memory and arithmetic sections, directed by the control section.

4. The answer (or answers) is sent to the output section and displayed to the programmer in an understandable form.

Not included in this simple model, but of course implied, are additional pieces of equipment that are necessary for operation. These include power supplies, mounting racks, air-conditioning units and so forth. Although these "accessory" devices are usually taken for granted, they must be carefully planned by the computer designer developing a computing system.

REVIEW QUESTIONS

1. Explain the meaning of the word "digital."
2. What is meant by the term "automatic computer"?
3. Contrast "digital" and "analog" computers.
4. List and describe the purpose and operation of the five basic functional sections of a digital computer.

2—Fundamentals of Computer Programming

The individual operations a computer can perform are very elementary, yet computers are routinely used to solve complex scientific and engineering problems. Their ability to do so is based almost completely on the ingenuity of the programmer.

Writing a program for a digital computer is somewhat of an art as well as a science — an art requiring lots of practice to master. There are often many ways to tackle a problem. A good programmer can spot the most direct route to the solution and set up a program which will be the most economical in terms of the number of individual instructions.

"The simpler, the better" is the programmer's motto, for it may cost several dollars a *minute* to run some of the larger computers. In addition, fewer instructions means that there are fewer chances for a mistake to be made.

WHAT PROGRAMMING IS

Roughly speaking, the programmer's job is to translate the details of a problem into a language the machine can understand and work with. Writing a program for a problem involves the following steps:

1. Stating the problem — most problems are stated in terms of mathematical equations and problem numbers. Occasionally, though, in business management problems, for example, no equation is directly available. In this case, the programmer must write a program based on what he wants the computer to do.

2. Breaking the problem down — the given problem numbers and equations must be arranged so that the solution can be arrived at through a sequence of simple arithmetic operations. We gave an example of this process in the last chapter.

3. Planning the solution — the individual operations are arranged so as to use the computer most efficiently. Here's where experience is important.

4. Programming — the actual "mechanics" of the programming operation in which a detailed step-by-step plan of operations is drawn up by enlarging the rough overall plans of Step 3. At this stage the program is carefully edited to check for errors.

5. Running the program — the program is fed into the computer along with problem numbers and other data, and the computer is set into operation.

An understanding of programming fundamentals is vital to an understanding of the digital computation process. Only after knowing what a computer should do can we intelligently set out to design one.

COMPUTER WORDS

The black box computer model described in the last chapter has five functional units: input section, output section, arithmetic section, control section and memory section. The functions of the input and output sections are obvious and will be taken for granted.

When a computer is calculating, the major flow of information takes place between the arithmetic and memory sections. These two sections form the calculating mechanism within the computer, and it is these two sections that the programmer is mainly concerned with. His instructions direct their operation, using the control section as a "middle man."

All information — instructions, problem numbers and intermediate results — is in the same form: groups of digits. These groups of digits may be problem numbers, such as the given values of constants in an equation; they may represent intermediate results; or they may be instructions, such as "add two numbers together." This means that written instructions must be translated or *coded* into a numerical form that the machine will understand. Much of the versatility of digital computers comes from the fact that instructions and problem data are entered into the machine in similar form.

Each group of digits, regardless of what it represents, is called a *computer word*. Therefore, there are two major kinds of computer words: *number words* and *instruction words*. Number words are simple, being only numbers that are used in the calculation. Instruction words are more complex, since they contain two pieces of information:

1. An *operation code number* that represents the command the computer will follow.

2. An *operation data address* that gives the memory address of the number word to be used during the operation.

In most simple computers, instruction words and number words are the same length, they contain the same number of digits. Generally speaking, the *precision* of a computer is proportional to its word length. A long word length means that problem numbers and intermediate results can be given to "many places."

As we said earlier, every memory location is assigned its own address. This address is a number. For example, the address numbers of a memory having 1000 cells would be three-digit numbers ranging from 000 to 999. Starting with 000 instead of 001 eliminates the fourth digit that would be necessary to specify 1000.

INSTRUCTIONS

The language a computer understands is called its *code*. The control section will respond to a properly coded instruction by carrying out the called-for operation.

Computer codes are similar, although no standard has been accepted by computer manufacturers. The code used in this chapter is not a real code, although it is representative of existing notations.

Computer programs may be very lengthy. In any case they are composed of data and instruction words which are groups of numbers. Since a sheet of numbers can be confusing, programmers have devised a set of word-like symbols that represent the different commands. These symbols are not part of the instructions, but are used to keep track of the various commands when planning a program "on paper."

The following table lists six basic computer operations. Others will be discussed later.

COMMAND	SYMBOL	OPERATION CODE NUMBER	MEANING
Clear And Add	CAD	01	Clear the arithmetic section and then add the number word stored at the specified operation data address.
Add	ADD	02	Add the number word stored at the specified operation data address to the number already in the arithmetic section.
Store	STR	03	Store the number in the arithmetic section in the specified operation data address.
Print Out	PRT	05	Print out (send to output section) the number in the arithmetic section.
Start Computer	START	08	Start the computer; get the address of the first instruction word from the specified operation data address.
Stop Computer	STOP	09	Stop the computer immediately.

WRITING A PROGRAM

Using these six instructions we can write a simple program that will add four numbers together.

Our first step is to choose memory locations for the four numbers so that they will be available to the arithmetic section during the calculation. We will assume that the computer has 1000 memory cells that can be used to store problem numbers and instructions. These cells are addressed 000 to 999, inclusive. Although the actual choice of address is quite arbitrary, it is good practice to group the problem numbers together in one block.

The four numbers and their memory addresses are:

Number	Address
621	100
48	101
72	102
235	103

The "plan" for solving this problem is very straightforward since only one kind of arithmetic operation is involved. First, the number 621 will be transferred to the arithmetic section. Then, the remaining three numbers will be added, one at a time, to form the final sum.

Selecting memory locations for the instruction words is also arbitrary. However, the instruction addresses must be sequential. If the first instruction is stored in cell 000, the second must be stored in 001, the third in 002, and so on. The reason for this is that the control section seeks new instructions in a sequential fashion. The START instruction tells the control section where to find the first instruction. From then on, the operation is automatic, and the control section will take each new instruction from the next-higher memory address after the old instruction has been carried out.

The program of instructions is shown below. Notice that each instruction word contains five "blank spaces" indicated by "X's." We have assumed a computer word length of ten digits — the operation code number accounts for the first two, and the operation data address makes up the last three, leaving five blank spaces. This may seem wasteful, but remember that the word length must be sufficient to accommodate large problem numbers.

Step	Symbol	Instruction Address	Instruction	Contents of Arithmetic Section
1.	START	000	08XXXXX001	0
2.	CAD	001	01XXXXX100	621
3.	ADD	002	02XXXXX101	669
4.	ADD	003	02XXXXX102	741
5.	ADD	004	02XXXXX103	976 = sum
6.	PRT	005	05XXXXXXX	976
7.	STOP	006	09XXXXXXX	976

sum = 976

Follow through this program step by step, consulting the instructions if necessary, until you fully understand the whys and hows of each step. The seven instructions cause the computer to add the four numbers as follows:

Instruction	Result
08XXXXX001	Starts computer; tells control section to go to address 001 for next instruction.
01XXXXX100	Clears arithmetic section; adds number word in address 100.
02XXXXX101	Adds number word in address 101 to number in arithmetic section.
02XXXXX102	Adds number word in address 102 to number in arithmetic section.
02XXXXX103	Adds number word in address 103 to number in arithmetic section.
05XXXXXXXX	Prints out (displays to programmer) number word in arithmetic section. (Note: this instruction has no operation data address.)
09XXXXXXXX	Stops computer.

The sixth instruction causes this answer to appear at the output section:

$$621 + 48 + 72 + 235 = 976$$

If this group of instructions were part of a larger program, and the sum was one of the intermediate results, we would have written a STR (store) instruction instead of the PRT (print out) instruction, and the sum would have been stored in the memory location specified by the operation data address.

ADDITIONAL OPERATIONS

A digital computer can also perform the other basic arithmetic operations, and if we know the correct instructions we can write programs containing them. The instructions for subtraction, multiplication and division are:

Command	Symbol	Operation Code Number	Meaning
Subtract	SUB	04	Subtract the number word stored at the specified operation data address from the number already in the arithmetic section.
Multiply	MUL	06	Multiply the number in the arithmetic section by the number word stored at the specified operation data address.

| Divide | DIV | 07 | Divide the number in the arithmetic section by the number word stored at the specified operation data address. |

A MORE COMPLEX PROGRAM

With the aid of these three additional instructions we can write a program to evaluate an equation similar to the one we discussed in the last chapter:

$$S = A \cdot X + \frac{B \cdot Y}{C} - D \cdot Z$$

In this equation, A, B, C and D are given constants; X, Y and Z are the variables; and S is the desired answer.

As before, we must specify the memory locations that will contain the problem numbers:

Term	Address	Term	Address
A	100	X	500
B	101	Y	501
C	102	Z	502
D	103		

The remaining memory locations are available for holding instruction words and intermediate answers. This program is different than the first example since it involves more than one arithmetic operation. The arithmetic section can only perform one kind of operation at a time, so it will be necessary to store intermediate results temporarily, until they are called for. As programmers, we must tell the computer where to store the intermediate results as well as what to do with them.

A straightforward program to evaluate the equation is:

STEP	SYMBOL	INSTRUCTION ADDRESS	INSTRUCTION	CONTENTS OF ARITHMETIC SECTION
1.	START	000	08XXXXX001	0
2.	CAD	001	01XXXXX500	X
3.	MUL	002	06XXXXX100	$A \cdot X$
4.	STR	003	03XXXXX900	$A \cdot X$
5.	CAD	004	01XXXXX501	Y
6.	MUL	005	06XXXXX101	$B \cdot Y$
7.	DIV	006	07XXXXX102	$B \cdot Y/C$
8.	STR	007	03XXXXX901	$B \cdot Y/C$
9.	CAD	008	01XXXXX502	Z
10.	MUL	009	06XXXXX103	$D \cdot Z$
11.	STR	010	03XXXXX902	$D \cdot Z$
12.	CAD	011	01XXXXX900	$A \cdot X$
13.	ADD	012	02XXXXX901	$A \cdot X + B \cdot Y/C$
14.	SUB	013	04XXXXX902	$A \cdot X + B \cdot Y/C - D \cdot Z$
15.	PRT	014	05XXXXXXXX	$A \cdot X + B \cdot Y/C - D \cdot Z$
16.	STOP	015	09XXXXXXXX	

INSTRUCTION	RESULT
08XXXXX001	Starts computer; tells control section to go to address 001 for next instruction.
01XXXXX500	Clears arithmetic section; adds number word in address 500.
06XXXXX100	Multiplies number in arithmetic section by the number word in address 100.
03XXXXX900	Stores contents of arithmetic section at address 900.
01XXXXX501	Clears arithmetic section; adds number word in address 501.
06XXXXX101	Multiplies number in arithmetic section by the number word in address 101.
07XXXXX102	Divides number in arithmetic section by the number word in address 102.
03XXXXX901	Stores contents of arithmetic section in address 901.
01XXXXX502	Clears arithmetic section; adds number word in address 502.
06XXXXX103	Multiplies number in arithmetic section by the number word in address 103.
03XXXXX902	Stores contents of arithmetic section in address 902.
01XXXXX900	Clears arithmetic section; adds number word in address 900.
02XXXXX901	Adds number word in 901 to number in arithmetic section.
04XXXXX902	Subtracts number word in 902 from number in arithmetic section.
05XXXXXXXX	Prints out number in arithmetic section.
09XXXXXXXX	Stops computer.

Memory locations 900, 901 and 902 are used to store temporarily the intermediate results of steps 4, 8 and 11, respectively. Notice that the STR operation only shifts a "replica" of the number in the arithmetic section to the specified memory location, the number itself is not disturbed. Once again, location 000 holds the first instruction. A total of fourteen instruction word locations, 000 through 013, are necessary.

Notice that we did not specify any values for the three variables X, Y and Z. In actual practice it might be necessary to solve this type of equation several thousand times, using new variables in each evaluation. It is important to realize that this program will work for any values of X, Y and Z that are stored in memory locations 500, 501 and 502, respectively. Thus, to evaluate the equation for different variables, the basic program can be rerun many times, with new variables in the correct memory locations for each run.

With the aid of *special operation instructions,* a digital computer can be programmed to change variables automatically, and repeat the basic program as many times as is desired. The different variable values are stored in the memory, and a new set is shifted to the correct locations at the start of each run. The application of this kind of programming to solve repetitive scientific and business problems is obvious. Without the aid of computers it wouldn't be possible to use many valuable engineering techniques because of the large number of individual but similar calculations involved.

JUMP INSTRUCTIONS

As engineering problems become more complex, the number of individual steps required to solve them on a computer increases. Straightforward programs, such as the two we have just discussed in which each step is individually planned and listed, become too long to be practical. Besides being cumbersome and difficult to work with, they may actually be too long to fit into the available memory locations.

Computer designers have rescued programmers from a sea of instructions with a group of special operations called *jump instructions:*

COMMAND	SYMBOL	OPERATION CODE NUMBER	MEANING
Jump	JUP	10	Go to the memory location specified in the operation data address for the next instruction.
Jump If Minus	JIM	11	Examine the number in the arithmetic section. If the number is positive (greater than or equal to 0) proceed with the next step of the program. If the number is negative (less than 0) go to the specified operation data address for the next instruction.

Jump instructions, often called *branch instructions,* allow a computer to alter its own program. The computer is not "thinking for itself," though, because it has been programmed to make these alterations.

In the course of ordinary operation the control section transfers new instructions from the memory in sequential fashion, as we have seen. If the first instruction is stored at memory address 000, the computer will look for the next instruction in location 001, and so on. When the computer comes upon a Jump (JUP) instruction as part of the program, it discards the original instruction address sequence, goes to the address indicated by the Jump instruction's operation data address for its next instruction, and carries on normally from there.

For example, a typical JUP instruction might look like this:

10XXXXX150

This instruction commands the computer to take its next instruction from memory address 150, the instruction after that from address 151, the next from 152, and so on. The JUP instruction has altered the sequence of instruction word addresses.

This kind of instruction can be used to make a program "recycle," or run over again. In this application the JUP instruction is the last instruction in the program. Its operation data address is the memory location of the first instruction in the program. Thus, when the computer reaches the JUP instruction, it is ordered to jump back to the first instruction, and it starts the program over again.

The Jump If Minus (JIM) command is an example of a *conditional* jump instruction. The control section obeys this kind of instruction only if certain conditions exist. When the computer comes upon a JIM instruction in the program, it examines the sign of the number in the arithmetic section. If the sign is a plus sign (the number is greater than or equal to zero), the jump command is ignored, and the computer proceeds with the normal sequence of instructions. If the sign is a minus sign (the number is negative), the control section obeys the jump command and takes its next instruction from the specified operation data address.

ADDING FROM 1 TO 100

To demonstrate the usefulness of the JUP instructions, let's write a program that will add together all of the integers between 1 and 100. In other words:

$$1 + 2 + 3 + 4 + 5 + 6 + \ldots + 98 + 99 + 100 = ?$$

We'll tackle this problem with our old programming methods first, so that we will be able to compare the end results.

After placing the 100 integers between 1 and 100 into one hundred memory locations, say 500 to 599, we can write the following program of 103 separate operations:

Step	Symbol	Instruction Address	Instruction	Contents of Arithmetic Section
1.	START	000	08XXXXX001	0
2.	CAD	001	01XXXXX500	1
3.	ADD	002	02XXXXX501	1 + 2
4.	ADD	003	02XXXXX502	1 + 2 + 3
.	.	.	.	
.	.	.	.	
.	.	.	.	
98.	ADD	097	02XXXXX596	... + 97

(Step)	(Symbol)	(Instruction Address)	(Instruction)	(Contents of Arithmetic Section)
99.	ADD	098	02XXXXX597	... + 97 + 98
100.	ADD	099	02XXXXX598	... + 97 + 98 + 99
101.	ADD	100	02XXXXX599	... + 97 + 98 + 99 + 100
102.	PRT	101	05XXXXXXXX	... + 97 + 98 + 99 + 100
103.	STOP	102	09XXXXXXXX	- - - - - - - -

A total of 203 memory locations are necessary to hold the instructions and problem numbers for the program in this form.

Notice that steps 2 to 100 are actually the same operation — addition — although a new number is added to the arithmetic section in each step. Notice, also, that there is a definite relationship between the numbers added in any two consecutive steps. The number added during any step is greater in value by 1 than the number added during the previous step. In step 2, the number 1 is added; in step 3, the number 2 is added; and so on. These observations will enable us to write a program containing only 13 instructions and requiring a total of 17 memory locations.

Since the numbers added in each operation are so simply related, it is a waste to store them in the memory. Rather, we can program the computer to *generate* the integers from 1 to 100 *as* it adds them together. The "mechanism" that will do this is a *subroutine* of 5 instructions. A subroutine is simply a part of a larger program that performs a "well-defined" operation. Typical subroutines are used to calculate trigonometric functions and convert between number systems.

The subroutine in our program will generate the integers between 1 and 100 by a simple, well-defined process: it will keep on adding 1's to generate successive integers. It starts with 1 and then adds 1 to generate 2. Next, it adds 1 to 2 to generate 3 and then adds 1 to 3 to generate 4. The process will continue indefinitely because a JUP instruction keeps the subroutine recycling, continuously producing successive integers.

A START instruction is used to start the subroutine running. After it has begun, the JUP instruction bypasses the starting step. The subroutine is as follows:

Step	Symbol	Instruction Address	Instruction	Contents of Arithmetic Section First Run	Second Run	N'th Run
1.	START	000	08XXXXX001	0	—	—
2.	CAD	001	01XXXXX100	0	1	N − 1
3.	ADD	002	02XXXXX101	1	2	N
4.	STR	003	03XXXXX100	1	2	N
5.	JUP	004	10XXXXX001	1	2	N

Location 101 contains 1
Location 100 contained 0 at the start of the first run

A little thought will verify that the number contained in memory location 100 increases by 1 during each run. If it contains 0 before the START instruction is given, it will contain "N" after the "N'th" run.

To complete the program we must add the following to the subroutine:

1. A set of instructions that will add the integers together as they are generated by the subroutine.
2. A "counter" that will stop the process after the 100th integer (100) has been added to the growing subtotal.

The complete program is shown on page 24. In the complete program instructions 5, 6 and 7 add the integers as they are generated. For each run, the "old" subtotal is transferred from location 500 to the arithmetic section, and there the integer generated by steps 2 to 4 is added to it. Then, the "new" subtotal is put into location 500.

Instructions 8, 9, 10 and 11 make up a "reverse counter." At the start of the process, location 900 contains 99. During each run, 1 is subtracted from the contents of location 900. After 100 runs, the subtraction will produce a negative number, which "activates" the JIM instruction, ending the operation. Until this happens, though, the JUP instruction keeps on recycling the operation by jumping the computer back to step 2.

REVIEW QUESTIONS

1. Define the following terms: word, operation code number, operation data address, code.
2. What is the difference between an instruction word and a number or data word? In what respects are they similar?
3. Explain the difference between the JUP and JIM instructions.
4. Numbers A, B, and C are in memory locations 100, 101 and 102, respectively. Write a program that will add them together and store the sum at address 500.
5. Write a program that will evaluate the equation $M = AX^2 + B$.
6. Explain what a subroutine is. Write the instructions for a subroutine that will generate only the *even* integers.
7. Numbers A, B and C are in memory locations 100, 101 and 102, respectively. Write a program that will evaluate $A \times B - C$, and print out the answer.
8. Modify the program given in the text so that it will add all the integers between 1 and 50 together.
9. Explain why the STOP and PRT instructions don't have operation data addresses, and why the START and STR instructions do.
10. Write a program that will transfer the contents of memory locations 100, 101 and 102 to memory locations 500, 501 and 502, respectively.

Step	Symbol	Instruction Address	Instruction	Contents of Arithmetic Section		
				First Run	100th Run	N'th Run
1.	START	000	08XXXXX001	0	–	–
2.	CAD	001	01XXXXX100	0	99	$N-1$
3.	ADD	002	02XXXXX101	1	100	N
4.	STR	003	03XXXXX100	1	100	N
5.	CAD	004	01XXXXX500	0	$+\ldots 98+99$	$+\ldots(N-2)+(N-1)$
6.	ADD	005	02XXXXX100	1	$+\ldots 98+100$	$+\ldots(N-1)+N$
7.	STR	006	03XXXXX500	1	$+\ldots 98+100$	$+\ldots(N-1)+N$
8.	CAD	007	01XXXXX900	99	0	$100-N$
9.	SUB	008	04XXXXX101	98	-1	$100-(N+1)$
10.	JIM	009	11XXXXX011	98	-1	$100-(N+1)$
11.	JUP	010	10XXXXX001	98	- - -	$100-(N+1)$
12.	CAD	011	01XXXXX500	- -	$+\ldots 99+100$	- - -
13.	PRT	012	05XXXXXXXX	- -	$+\ldots 99+100$	- - -
14.	STOP	013	09XXXXXXXX			

At the start of the process:

Location	Contains
101	1
900	99
500	0
100	0

During the process:

Location	Is Used to Store
100	Integers being generated
500	Sum of integers added so far

At the end of the process:

Location	Contains
101	(still contains) 1
900	-1
500	Sum of all the integers from 1 to 100
100	100

3—The Binary Number System

Our simple "black box" model helped to introduce us to the basic principles of digital computation. But to understand the detailed operation of a digital computer, we must look inside the black boxes and study the computer's "vital organs."

What do digital computers do? They solve numerical problems accurately, at high speed. Fast operation is vital so that lengthy problems involving many individual steps can be handled quickly. Notice, though, that accuracy must come before speed; incorrect answers are worthless no matter how fast they are obtained.

How do digital computers solve problems? As we have seen, they manipulate numbers according to a program of instructions. Computer operation consists of a continuous flow of numbers — both numerically coded instructions and problem data — within the machine.

We can conclude, then, that a computer's "organs" are circuits built to manipulate numbers. Before we can study these circuits we must understand the manner in which numbers are represented by circuit components. A good starting point is the study of numbers themselves.

NUMBER SYSTEMS

A *number system* is a set of symbols that represent quantity. The decimal system (or Arabic system, named after its inventors) is familiar to every reader, and will be used to illustrate the principles of number systems in general. Each individual symbol is called a *digit,* and is given its own name. The decimal system, as we know, has ten digits: 0, 1, 2, 3, 4, 5, 6, 7, 8 and 9. In addition, a number system has a set of rules that tells how to arrange the digits to form *numbers.* A number is a group of digits arranged according to these rules.

25

Although we have only ten digits to work with in the decimal system, we can write numbers that express all quantities, no matter how large or small they may be. This is possible because of *positional notation*. The value of any digit depends on its relative position within a number. The digits of the number 3333 are identical, and yet each has a different value: the first "3" (from right to left) refers to the "units" column, the second to the "tens" column, the third to the "hundreds" column, and the fourth to the "thousands" column. Read aloud, 3333 sounds like "three thousand, three hundred and thirty three." In other words, 3333 is just a compact way of writing

$$3 \text{ thousand} + 3 \text{ hundred} + \text{thirty} + \text{three}$$

or

$$3 \times (1000) + 3 \times (100) + 3 \times (10) + 3 \times (1)$$

or

$$3 \times (10^3) + 3 \times (10^2) + 3 \times (10^1) + 3 \times (10^0)$$

Notice that the familiar term "column" actually refers to ascending multiples, or powers of 10. The units column refers to 10^0 (or 1); the tens column to 10^1 (or 10); the hundreds column to 10^2 (or 100); and the thousands column to 10^3 (or 1000); and so forth.

The number 10 is called the *base* or *radix* of the decimal system. The base number of any positional notation number system is equal to the number of digits it contains.

All arithmetic is straightforward in our decimal system. After learning a few simple rules, and memorizing the addition and multiplication "tables," it's easy to perform any calculation. This is true in regard to any positional notation system, and, as we shall see, there are several.

Legend has it that our number system has ten digits because men have ten fingers. This may be so, but there is nothing magical about the number 10. Any number greater than 1 may be used as the base number of a positional notation number system. The *octal* number system, for example, is constructed by using 8 as the base number. Therefore, there are only eight digits in the octal system: 0, 1, 2, 3, 4, 5, 6 and 7. The decimal symbols 8 and 9 are meaningless in this system and aren't used.

Octal numbers are formed in the same way as decimal numbers. The only difference is that multiples (or powers) of 8 are used instead of multiples of 10. The octal number 1521 represents the same quantity as the decimal number 849, as shown below:

$$\begin{aligned} \text{octal } 1521 &= 1 \times (8^3) + 5 \times (8^2) + 2 \times (8^1) + 1 \times (8^0) \\ &= 1 \times 512 + 5 \times 64 + 2 \times 8 + 1 \times 1 \\ &= \text{decimal } 849 \end{aligned}$$

Another example:

$$\text{octal } 625 = 6 \times (8^2) + 2 \times (8^1) + 5 \times (8^0)$$
$$= 6 \times 64 \ \ + 2 \times 8 \ \ \ \ + 5 \times 1$$
$$= \text{decimal } 405$$

To avoid confusion when dealing with two number systems at the same time, parentheses and a subscript will be used to indicate the base of a number. For example, decimal 18 will be written $(18)_{10}$, which means 18 "to the base 10." Similarly, octal 25 is written $(25)_8$, meaning that the number 25 has a base number of 8.

The *quinary* number system is built on the base 5, and therefore has only five digits: 0, 1, 2, 3 and 4. Quinary numbers are formed in the same way as decimal numbers, except that powers of 5 replace the powers of 10. For example:

$$\text{quinary } 1234 = (1234)_5 = 1 \times (5^3) + 2 \times (5^2) + 3 \times (5^1) + 4 \times (5^0)$$
$$= 1 \times 125 \ + 2 \times 25 \ \ \ + 3 \times 5 \ \ \ + 4 \times 1$$
$$= (194)_{10} = \text{decimal } 194$$

Another example:

$$\text{quinary } 444 = (444)_5 = 4 \times (5^2) + 4 \times (5^1) + 4 \times (5^0)$$
$$= 4 \times 25 \ \ \ \ + 4 \times 5 \ \ \ + 4 \times 1$$
$$= (124)_{10} = \text{decimal } 124$$

The *binary* number system has a base of 2; the positions of the digits in a binary number refer to increasing powers of 2. Only two digits are required in order to write a binary number: 0 and 1.

In the binary system, $(14)_{10}$ becomes $(1110)_2$, as shown below:

$$\text{binary } 1110 = (1110)_2 = 1 \times (2^3) + 1 \times (2^2) + 1 \times (2^1) + 0 \times (2^0)$$
$$= 1 \times 8 \ \ \ + 1 \times 4 \ \ \ + 1 \times 2 \ \ \ + 0 \times 1$$
$$= (14)_{10} = \text{decimal } 14$$

Another example:

$$\text{binary } 101011 = (101011)_2$$
$$= 1 \times (2^5) + 0 \times (2^4) + 1 \times (2^3) + 0 \times (2^2) + 1 \times (2^1)$$
$$+ 1 \times (2^0)$$
$$= 1 \times 32 + 0 \times 16 + 1 \times 8 + 0 \times 4 + 1 \times 2 + 1 \times 1$$
$$= (43)_{10} = \text{decimal } 43$$

The binary number system may seem confusing at first, but it is actually quite simple. It takes time to become accustomed to working with only two digits instead of ten. As we shall soon see, numbers written in the binary number system are in a perfect form to be manipulated by electronic circuits. Consequently, digital computers are designed to perform arithmetic in the binary number system, or some modification of it.

CIRCUITS AND NUMBERS

Ideally, a digital computer should work directly in the decimal number system. Unfortunately, the characteristics of high-speed electronic circuits make the ideal impractical. Let's see why.

We learned in Chapter 1 that digital mechanisms actually represent, within themselves, the numbers being manipulated. Pascal's adding machine, for example, represented the numbers with notched wheels. Each wheel had ten notches — one notch for each decimal digit.

Pascal's calculator demonstrates a fundamental principle of digital computer design: the calculating mechanisms must be able to represent all of the digits of the number system that the calculations are being made in.

This principle makes sense. Just as we jot down numbers on paper to represent them when we do arithmetic, a computer must have some way of representing numbers within itself as it calculates.

Ancient mathematicians coined ten separate symbols, or characters, to represent the decimal digits, and we must be able to recognize and write them all in order to do decimal arithmetic. In the same way, a computer calculating in the decimal system must be able to represent all of the individual decimal digits.

What does this mean? Simply, that digital computer circuits must be able to assume a *different and recognizable state* for each digit they work with. Decimal arithmetic involves ten digits, so the circuits must have ten such states — one for each digit — to be able to compute in the decimal system.

Most non-automatic mechanical digital calculators (adding machines, cash registers, odometers, etc.) operate directly in the decimal number system. It's relatively easy to manufacture high precision gears having ten teeth, each tooth representing one digit. Modern desk calculators are highly sophisticated mechanisms that use this kind of component.

Mechanical devices, however, can not be made to run at the ultra-high speeds at which digital computers must operate, so designers have turned to electro-mechanical and electronic components. Early automatic digital computers were constructed of relays. These were soon made obsolete by vacuum tube equipped computers, which are now being replaced by transistorized computers.

Obviously, there is a big difference between gears and relays, or notched wheels and vacuum tubes! Electro-mechanical components, including relays and other switch-like devices, are fundamentally *bistable* in nature. That is, they have two stable operating states. A relay can be energized or not energized; a switch can be "on" or "off." There usually isn't any in-between.

Because these components have only two states, they can not be used in calculating mechanisms that work in the decimal system.

Vacuum tubes and transistors, on the other hand, can assume an infinite number of states depending on power supply and bias voltages. It's possible to construct a circuit using a single vacuum tube or transistor that will have ten discrete operating states. Unfortunately, these circuits are not very reliable. As the tube or transistor ages, or if any of the power supply voltages vary, the ten operating points will shift around. This means that the "discrete" states are no longer discrete. Keep in mind the requirement that computers must be accurate. Accuracy and reliability go hand in hand.

To insure reliability, computer designers treat vacuum tubes and transistors as switch-like devices (see Chapter 5) having two states: fully conducting and non-conducting. The fully conducting state is similar to the "on" state of a switch; the non-conducting state is similar to "off."

Consider an ordinary light bulb. The brightness can be varied by controlling the filament voltage. Ten different voltages will produce ten different brightness levels in a *new* bulb. As the bulb gets older, however, all the brightness levels will get dimmer and it will become increasingly difficult to tell them apart.

It would always be very easy, though, to tell if the lamp were "on" or "off." This is true of most other circuit components. It's difficult to recognize varying degrees of "on," but it's very easy to distinguish between "on" and "off."

Since reliable operation limits the available number of discrete operating states of high speed circuitry to two ("on" and "off"), electronic computers cannot calculate directly in the decimal number system. Instead, they perform arithmetic using binary numbers. You'll recall that the binary number system (base $= 2$) has only two digits, 0 and 1. If one of the operating states is used to represent 1, and the other 0, the requirement that "the calculating mechanism be able to represent all the digits it is working with" is met. Usually, "on" stands for 1, and "off" stands for 0.

BINARY NUMBERS

You probably have noticed that small-base number systems use more of their digits to express a given quantity than large-base systems. The decimal number $(87)_{10}$, for example, is equivalent to $(127)_8$, or $(322)_5$ or $(1010111)_2$. Any advantage that this may give to high-base numbers is counterbalanced by the fact that arithmetic is much simpler to perform in low-base number systems. Binary arithmetic is the easiest of them all. Binary multiplication contains only four combinations, as compared with the one hundred used in the decimal multiplication table.

Let's quickly review the binary notation. Binary numbers are written using 2 as the base or radix. Each of the "columns" refers to a power of 2.

The rules of number formation are the same as in the more familiar decimal number system. To illustrate:

$$\text{binary } 1010111 = (1010111)_2$$
$$= 1 \times (2^6) + 0 \times (2^5) + 1 \times (2^4) + 0 \times (2^3) + 1 \times (2^2)$$
$$+ 1 \times (2^1) + 1 \times (2^0)$$
$$= 1 + 64 + 0 \times 32 + 1 \times 16 + 0 \times 8 + 1 \times 4 + 1 \times 2$$
$$+ 1 \times 1$$
$$= (87)_{10} = \text{decimal } 87$$

Incidentally, the binary number $(1101)_2$ is read aloud as "one - one - zero - one," *not* as "one thousand one hundred and eleven."

The following table lists the first thirty-one binary numbers, and a few high-value binary numbers, together with their decimal equivalent. Work your way through the list number by number if you are at all hazy about binary number formation. A solid knowledge of binary number basics is "a must" if you wish to understand digital computer arithmetic.

Binary Number	Decimal Equivalent	Binary Number	Decimal Equivalent
0	0	10010	18
1	1	10011	19
10	2	10100	20
11	3	10101	21
100	4	10110	22
101	5	10111	23
110	6	11000	24
111	7	11001	25
1000	8	11010	26
1001	9	11011	27
1010	10	11100	28
1011	11	11101	29
1100	12	11110	30
1101	13	11111	31
1110	14	1000000	64
1111	15	1100110011001	6553
10000	16	11111111111111	16383
10001	17		

Fractional numbers can also be expressed in binary notation. As might be expected, they are formed by sums of *negative* powers of 2. All binary digits to the right of the *binary point* (the binary equivalent of the decimal point) refer to negative powers. For example:

$$(0.001)_2 = 0 \times (2^{-1}) + 0 \times (2^{-2}) + 1 \times (2^{-3})$$
$$= 0 \times \tfrac{1}{2} + 0 \times \tfrac{1}{4} + 1 \times \tfrac{1}{8}$$
$$= (\tfrac{1}{8})_{10}$$

Another example:

$$(0.0101)_2 = 0 \times (2^{-1}) + 1 \times (2^{-2}) + 0 \times (2^{-3}) + 1 \times (2^{-4})$$
$$= 0 \times \tfrac{1}{2} \quad + 1 \times \tfrac{1}{4} \quad + 0 \times \tfrac{1}{8} \quad + 1 \times \tfrac{1}{16}$$
$$= 0 \times (\tfrac{5}{16})_{10}$$

Here are ten more binary fractions and their decimal equivalents:

BINARY FRACTION	DECIMAL EQUIVALENT
0.1	1/2
0.01	1/4
0.0001	1/16
0.11	3/4
0.011	3/8
0.101	5/8
0.111	7/8
0.1001	9/16
0.1101	13/16
0.1111	15/16

The binary point is treated exactly as the decimal point is in decimal number system computations. "Mixed" binary numbers look like this:

$$(101.01)_2 = (5\tfrac{1}{4})_{10}$$
$$(10010.1101)_2 = (18\tfrac{13}{16})_{10}$$

CONVERTING DECIMAL NUMBERS TO BINARY NUMBERS

Several examples in this chapter have illustrated the simple addition method used to convert binary numbers to their decimal equivalents. Since the method is self explanatory, nothing more will be said about it. Traveling the other way, though — from decimal notation to binary — the going gets a bit trickier.

The simplest way to convert a decimal number to its binary equivalent is to repeatedly subtract decreasing powers of 2 from the number until nothing remains. The binary number is written by placing a 1 in every column position that corresponds to a power of 2 that was subtracted; a 0 is placed in the position corresponding to powers of 2 that weren't used. The first step is to determine the largest power of 2 that is smaller than or equal to the decimal number. This power of 2 is then subtracted from the number, leaving the "first difference."

The next step is to determine the largest power of 2 that is smaller than or equal to the first difference. This power of 2 is subtracted, leaving the "second difference."

This process of forming differences and then subtracting powers of 2 continues until the "final difference" equals 0.

As an example, let's convert $(43)_{10}$ to its binary equivalent:

Step

1. Largest power of 2 smaller than $43 = 2^5 = 32$
$$43 - 32 = 11 \quad \text{(first difference)}$$

2. Largest power of 2 smaller than $11 = 2^3 = 8$
$$11 - 8 = 3 \quad \text{(second difference)}$$

3. Largest power of 2 smaller than $3 = 2^1 = 2$
$$3 - 2 = 1 \quad \text{(third difference)}$$

4. Largest power of 2 equal to $1 = 2^0 = 1$
$$1 - 1 = 0 \quad \text{(final difference)}$$

The powers of 2 that were subtracted are 2^5, 2^3, 2^1 and 2^0. Writing 1 in the columns corresponding to these powers, and 0 in the other columns, we find that:

$$(43)_{10} = (101011)_2$$

This method can also be used to convert decimal, mixed and fractional numbers to their binary equivalent. Watch out though, or you'll trip over the binary point: 2^{-1} is a larger power of 2 than 2^{-2}.

A BETTER DECIMAL-BINARY CONVERSION METHOD

The method just described has one or two shortcomings. It assumes that you know all the powers of 2, or at least have a table on hand; and it becomes very inconvenient when large powers of two and many subtractions are necessary. As a result, the repeated subtraction conversion method is only used for small decimal numbers, when it can be done "mentally."

A second method, suitable for converting large decimal numbers, consists of repeatedly dividing the decimal number by 2. Because we are dividing by 2, the remainder of any division can only be 0 or 1. These remainders are the digits of the binary equivalent.

The remainder of the first division is written in the 2^0 column; the remainder of the second in the 2^1; the remainder of the third in the 2^2; and so on. For example, to convert $(69)_{10}$:

Division	Dividend	Remainder
1	$69/2 = 34$	1
2	$34/2 = 17$	0
3	$17/2 = 8$	1
4	$8/2 = 4$	0
5	$4/2 = 2$	0
6	$2/2 = 1$	0
7	$1/2 = 0$	1

Placing the remainders in their proper columns we find that:

$$(69)_{10} = (1000101)_2$$

To check this answer, let's convert the binary number back to decimal form by the usual method:

$$(1000101)_2 = 1 \times (2^6) + 0 \times (2^5) + 0 \times (2^4) + 0 \times (2^3) + 1 \times (2^2)$$
$$+ 0 \times (2^1) + 1 \times (2^0)$$
$$= 1 \times 64 + 0 \times 32 + 0 \times 16 + 0 \times 8 + 1 \times 4 + 0 \times 2$$
$$+ 1 \times 1$$
$$= (69)_{10}$$

This method will *not* work on mixed decimal numbers.

BINARY CODED DECIMAL NUMBERS

As we said earlier, it would be desirable for a digital computer to manipulate decimal numbers directly. Since this isn't possible, a compromise is often made, and decimal numbers are represented in the computer in a binary *coded* form.

There are several *binary codes* for decimal numbers in common use. They all represent individual decimal digits with a group of four binary digits. Thus it takes 8 binary digits (two groups of 4) to represent a two-digit decimal number. The code illustrated below is called the *natural binary decimal code*.

DECIMAL DIGIT	BINARY CODE
0	0000
1	0001
2	0010
3	0011
4	0100
5	0101
6	0110
7	0111
8	1000
9	1001

The following examples illustrate how this code represents decimal numbers:

Decimal Number	Coded Form
285	0010-1000-0101
63	0110-0011
1771	0001-0111-0111-0001
409	0100-0000-1001

The dash marks are shown in the coded numbers for clarity, they don't appear inside a computer.

Binary codes enable the computer circuits to handle decimal numbers by treating each decimal digit as an individual binary number. It isn't necessary to convert the decimal number into its binary number equivalent. In the last chapter, we programmed a computer having a word length of ten decimal digits. A typical number word is shown below in both its decimal and binary coded decimal form. Notice that forty binary digits are required to code a ten-decimal digit number:

$$1875900234 = \text{decimal form}$$

$$0001\text{-}1000\text{-}0111\text{-}0101\text{-}1001\text{-}0000\text{-}0000\text{-}0010\text{-}0011\text{-}0100 = \text{binary coded form}$$

BINARY ADDITION

As we said earlier, the binary arithmetic operations are much simpler to perform than their decimal number system equivalents. However, the "rules" of arithmetic are identical in both systems.

The binary addition table, which lists *all* of the possible combinations that can occur when two binary digits are added, contains only four entries:

$$
\begin{array}{r} 0 \\ + 0 \\ \hline 0 \end{array}
\qquad\qquad
\begin{array}{r} 0 \\ + 1 \\ \hline 1 \end{array}
$$

$$
\begin{array}{r} 0 \\ + 1 \\ \hline 1 \end{array}
\qquad\qquad
\begin{array}{r} 1 \\ + 1 \\ \hline 0 \end{array} \text{ plus a carry-over of 1}
$$

Notice that a "carry-over" is produced when 1 and 1 are added. Binary carry-overs are treated in the same fashion as decimal carry-overs; they are carried-over to the left. In other words, 1 plus 1 equals 2, but since 1 is the largest available binary digit, 2 must be written as 10.

Binary addition is performed by following the rules shown in the binary addition table:

Decimal	Binary		Decimal	Binary
3	11		23	10111
+ 2	+ 10		+ 7	+ 111
5	101		30	11110
12	1100		15	1111
+ 16	+ 10000		+ 3	+ 11
28	11100		18	10010

When adding two large binary numbers, keeping track of the various carry-overs becomes a confusing task. One way to simplify matters is to form the *partial sum* first, and add the carry-overs later. At its name suggests, the partial sum is not the final answer. It is formed by adding two binary numbers and temporarily putting the carry-overs aside. For example:

$$
\begin{array}{r}
27 \\
+\ 14 \\
\hline
41
\end{array}
\qquad
\begin{array}{r}
11011 \\
+\ 1110 \\
\hline
10101 \quad \text{(partial sum)} \\
1\ 1 \quad \text{(carry-overs)} \\
\hline
101001 \quad \text{(full sum)}
\end{array}
$$

As shown above, the *full sum* is found by adding the carry-overs to the proper columns of the partial sum.

Binary mixed numbers are added in the same way as decimal mixed numbers. The binary point is always kept in the same position:

Decimal	Binary	Decimal	Binary
$7\ \frac{1}{16}$	111.0001	$4\frac{1}{2}$	100.1
$+\ 6\ \frac{1}{8}$	$+$ 110.0010	$+\ 8\frac{1}{4}$	$+$ 1000.01
$13\ \frac{3}{16}$	1101.0011	$12\frac{3}{4}$	1100.11

BINARY SUBTRACTION   1254356

The binary subtraction table also contains only four entries:

$$
\begin{array}{r}
0 \\
-\ 0 \\
\hline
0
\end{array}
\qquad\qquad
\begin{array}{r}
1 \\
-\ 1 \\
\hline
0
\end{array}
$$

$$
\begin{array}{r}
1 \\
-\ 0 \\
\hline
1
\end{array}
\qquad\qquad
\begin{array}{r}
0 \\
-\ 1 \\
\hline
1
\end{array}
\quad \text{with a "borrow" of 1}
$$

Just as in decimal subtraction, a "borrow" must be made in order to subtract a larger digit from a smaller one. Since there are only two binary digits, this only happens when 1 is subtracted from 0. In this case, a 1 is borrowed from the next column to the left.

All binary subtraction, including mixed number problems, is performed according to this table. The following examples will illustrate the binary subtraction process:

Decimal	Binary	Decimal	Binary
15	1111	8	1000
− 12	− 1100	− 3	− 11
3	11	5	101

Decimal	Binary	Decimal	Binary
31	11111	7½	11.10
− 15	− 1111	− 2¾	− 10.11
16	10000	4¾	100.11

One rule that computer designers always follow is that a digital computer must be simplified whenever possible. Although a computer can be built to perform binary subtraction in the manner shown above, to do so would add unnecessary circuitry to the arithmetic section. With the use of *complements,* subtraction can be reduced to an addition operation.

Subtraction through addition may seem like magic, but it really isn't. The complement subtraction method is well known, but it's simply too cumbersome to be worthwhile when used in the decimal system. However, it is a very simple operation to perform in the binary number system.

Let's first study the process in the decimal system. The "9's complement (or simply "complement") of any digit is defined as the difference between the digit and 9. Therefore, the complement of 4 is 5 ($9 − 4 = 5$) and the complement of 8 is 1 ($9 − 8 = 1$). Finding the complement of a digit is known as "complementing" that digit.

The complement of a number may be found by complementing each of its digits individually. Thus, to complement 123456789:

$$
\begin{array}{rl}
  & 9\,9\,9\,9\,9\,9\,9\,9\,9 \\
- & 1\,2\,3\,4\,5\,6\,7\,8\,9 \quad \text{(number)} \\
\hline
  & 8\,7\,6\,5\,4\,3\,2\,1\,0 \quad \text{(complement)}
\end{array}
$$

Subtraction using complements is performed by following these two simple rules:

1. *Add* the complement of the subtrahend to the minuend.
2. If there is a final carry-over, add it to the least significant digit (the right-hand digit).

For example:

Regular Subtraction		Complement Method	
153	(minuend)	153	(minuend)
− 042	(subtrahend)	957	(complement of 042)
111	(difference)	1 110	(sum of minuend and complement of 042)
		1	(final carry)
		111	(difference)

Notice that the minuend and the subtrahend must have the same number of digits. Thus, in the above example, a 0 was placed in front of 42 to make it 042 and give it three digits, since 153 has three digits. The following examples will provide additional illustrations:

Regular Subtraction		Complement Method	
75	(minuend)	75	(minuend)
− 22	(subtrahend)	+ 77	(complement of 22)
53	(difference)	⌐1 51	(sum of minuend and complement of 22)
		└→ 1	(final carry)
		53	(difference)

10,120	(minuend)	10,120	(minuend)
− 07,485	(subtrahend)	+ 92,514	(complement of 07,485)
2,635	(difference)	⌐1 02,634	(sum of minuend and complement of 07,485)
		└→ 1	(final carry)
		2,635	(difference)

This process can be performed in the binary number system, except the "1's" complement replaces the "9's" complement notation. The 1's complement of a binary digit is found by subtracting the digit from 1. However, since $1 - 0 = 1$ (complement of $0 = 1$), and $1 - 1 = 0$ (complement of $1 = 0$), the complement of any binary number can be written simply by replacing all the 0's with 1's, and all the 1's with 0's. For example:

the complement of $111000111 = 000111000$

and

the complement of $10101010 = 01010101$

The same rules described above for the decimal system apply to the complement method of subtraction in the binary system. Adding the final carry-over digit to the least significant digit is usually called the *end-around carry* operation. The following examples will illustrate the correct procedure:

Decimal		Binary	
15		1111	(minuend)
− 12		0011	(complement of 1100)
3		⌐1 0010	(sum of minuend and complement of 1100)
		└→ 1	(end-around carry)
		11	(difference)

Decimal		Binary	
31		11111	(minuend)
− 15		10000	(complement of 01111)
16		┌─1 01111	(sum of minuend and complement of 01111)
		└──→1	(end-around carry)
		10000	(difference)

BINARY MULTIPLICATION

The binary multiplication table is very short; it contains only four entries. Actually, these four can be further reduced to two easy-to-learn rules: the product of $1 \times 1 = 1$; all other multiplications equal 0. The complete multiplication table is:

$$
\begin{array}{r} 0 \\ \times\ 0 \\ \hline 0 \end{array}
\qquad\qquad
\begin{array}{r} 0 \\ \times\ 1 \\ \hline 0 \end{array}
$$

$$
\begin{array}{r} 1 \\ \times\ 0 \\ \hline 0 \end{array}
\qquad\qquad
\begin{array}{r} 1 \\ \times\ 1 \\ \hline 1 \end{array}
$$

The reason for this simplicity is readily apparent: the product of 0 and any other digit is always 0. Since the only other binary digit is 1, three out of the four possible products (0×1, 0×0, 1×0) must equal 0. Two binary numbers are multiplied in the same way as two decimal numbers. This simple procedure is illustrated below:

Decimal		Binary	
15		1111	(multiplicand)
× 6		× 110	(multiplier)
90		0000	
		1111	(partial products)
		1111	
		1011010	(product)

7		111	(multiplicand)
× 4		× 100	(multiplier)
28		000	
		000	(partial products)
		111	
		11100	(product)

As these examples show, binary multiplication involves a series of *shifts* and additions of the partial products. The partial products are easily found since they are either equal to the multiplicand or to 0. Every 1 in the multiplier produces a partial product equal to the multiplicand, and every 0 in the multiplier produces a partial product equal to 0. Each successive partial product is shifted one position to the left of the partial product directly above it.

Shift operations are used to multiply or divide binary numbers by 2: a rightwards shift of one position divides by 2; a leftwards shift of one position multiplies by 2. For example:

$$(1010)_2 = (10)_{10}$$
$$(10100)_2 = (20)_{10} \quad \text{— shift left one position}$$
$$(101)_2 = (5)_{10} \quad \text{— shift right one position}$$

Binary shift operations are analogous to shifts in the decimal system: a rightwards shift of one position of a decimal number divides it by 10; a leftwards shift of one position multiplies it by 10.

BINARY DIVISION

Binary division is performed in the same way as decimal "long division." It's much simpler, though, because the binary division table lists only two combinations:

$$\frac{0}{1} = 0 \qquad\qquad \frac{1}{1} = 1$$

Division by 0 (1/0 or 0/0) is meaningless in the binary number system, just as it is in the decimal system. The following examples illustrate the binary division process:

Decimal

```
      2
3 ) 6
```

Binary

```
        10
11 ) 110
       11
        0
```

Decimal

```
      7
4 ) 28
```

Binary

```
        111
100 ) 11100
       100
       110
       100
       100
       100
         0
```

REVIEW QUESTIONS

1. How many digits must be represented by the calculating mechanisms of digital computers built to calculate in the following number systems: decimal; octal; quinary; binary?

2. Convert the following binary numbers to their decimal equivalents: 110010; 10010; 11111; 1010101011; 11011.

3. Convert the following decimal numbers to their binary equivalents: 74; 123; 26; 91; 48.

4. Convert the following decimal numbers to their binary *coded* form: 85; 235; 456; 700; 399.911.

5. Convert the following binary *coded* numbers to their decimal form: 0011-1000-0111 ; 1001-1001 ; 0101-0000-0000-0100 ; 0011-0001-0110-1001 ; 0011-0101-1000-1001 .

6. Multiply the following pairs of binary numbers: 110110 $\times$ 101 ; 1001 $\times$ 10 ; 11111 $\times$ 10101 ; 100000 $\times$ 11111 ; 1010 $\times$ 110.

7. Find the sum of the following binary numbers (add them all together): 110011 + 11111111 + 100000 + 10101010 + 101 + 1011100

8. Perform the following binary divisions: 1111111 / 101 ; 1100 / 100 ; 100100 / 1001 ; 10010 / 11 ; 1100100 / 1010.

9. Perform the following binary subtractions using the direct method: 101110011 − 1010; 1111111 − 11001; 100010 − 11100; 1100101 − 101; 11111011 − 101010.

10. Perform the following binary subtractions using the complement addition method: 1010111 − 1101 ; 11111 − 11 ; 101100011 − 10111 ; 1000011 − 11111 ; 11100011 − 101110.

4 — An Introduction to Logical Design Techniques

The front cover suggests that this book is concerned with electronic digital computers. Yet, three chapters have gone by without a hint of a schematic diagram or reference to a circuit description. Probably, many readers are anxious to examine the circuitry of the five computer sections; to jump right in, so to speak, and see how a real machine is put together.

They would be a little disappointed and very surprised if they did. Although an electronic computer may contain tens of thousands of individual electronic parts, the heart of this complex device consists of hundreds of identical circuits wired together. The calculating sections of most computers are designed using only five basic circuits: the *AND gate,* the *OR gate,* the *bistable circuit,* the *inverter,* and the *delay.* (The operation of these circuits is described in Chapter 5.)

You've probably noticed that digital computation consists of two separate but closely related groups of operations going on simultaneously inside a computer: the actual numerical calculations performed by the arithmetic section; and the group of operations that takes place in the control section, where the numerically coded instructions are interpreted and the commands they contain are executed.

Both groups of operations are similar in that they both involve a flow of binary (or binary coded decimal) numbers. Problem numbers flow into the arithmetic section, and intermediate results flow back into memory for temporary storage. Instruction words flow between memory and control, and in turn cause the flow of more problem and instruction numbers. Numbers are also in motion inside the arithmetic section. As we have seen, the binary arithmetic operations involve shifts, carry-overs and borrows.

41

Since digital computation is based on the controlled movement of binary numbers, we might reason that the five basic computer circuits control the flow of binary numbers. More precisely, they control the movement of electrical signals that represent the binary digits.

BITS

Throughout our study of binary numbers we found it convenient to represent the two binary digits with the decimal symbols 0 and 1. These were fine for pencil and paper calculation, but totally different symbols, based on electrical signals instead of written characters, are necessary to represent the binary digits within the calculating and control circuitry of a computer.

Back in the days when computer technology was a young science, the word *bit* was coined. Bit is a contraction of the two words *BI*nary and digi*T*. Since all information flowing within a computer is in binary number form, the bit is the "basic stuff" computer information is composed of. A single bit is the smallest unit of information a computer deals with. In much the same way that matter is built up of atoms, computer information is built up of bits. Maintaining computer accuracy boils down to a careful and faithful handling of each individual bit of information.

What are the characteristics required of the two electrical signals that represent the two binary digits, or bits? First, they must be suitable for use with high-speed circuitry. Second, the two signals must be very easy to tell apart. Finally, the signals must be hard to confuse with each other.

The difference between the two last similar-sounding characteristics is important and worth noting. All electronic circuits, to varying degrees, distort electrical signals that pass through them. It is usually very easy to distinguish between two slightly dissimilar electrical signals just after they have been generated, but the same two signals might look confusingly alike after they have passed through some circuitry. Accuracy demands that the signals representing the two bits always be recognizable, regardless of how far they have traveled through the calculating and control circuits.

Many pairs of electrical signals meet these three requirements. The following table lists several that are in use today:

1 Bit	0 Bit
Positive pulse	No pulse (or negative pulse)
Negative pulse	No pulse (or positive pulse)
Positive voltage	Zero voltage (or negative voltage)
Negative voltage	Zero voltage (or positive voltage)
Positive current	Zero current
High voltage	Low voltage

Often, two or more signal pairs may be used in a single computer. Voltage levels usually represent the bits in the various circuits, while pulses are used to transmit information from one circuit to another.

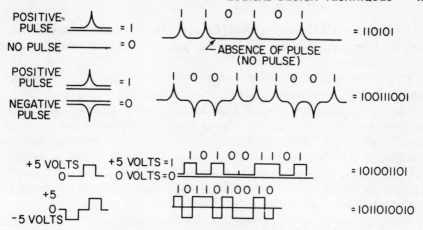

FIG. 4-1. (top) Representing binary numbers with electrical signals. (bottom) When voltage levels are used to represent binary digits, the respective levels are often called **logic levels.**

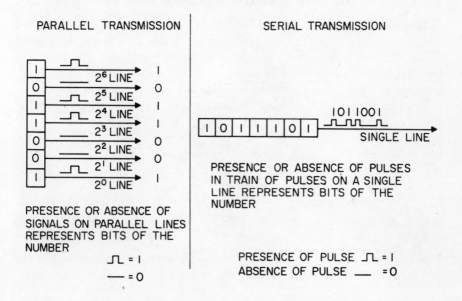

FIG. 4-2. Transmitting binary numbers within a computer.

THE TRANSMISSION OF BITS

Following a program requires that complete binary numbers, composed of many individual bits, be shuffled around inside a computer. One often-used method consists of transmitting each of the bits along a separate wire. This method is called *parallel transmission*. Ten lines would be necessary to transmit a ten bit binary number, for example. Each of the parallel transmission lines corresponds to one of the "columns," or powers of 2, of the binary number.

Parallel transmission is fairly complicated but very fast, since a complete binary number is transmitted between two circuits at once.

The other commonly used number transmission method is called *serial transmission*. Here, the signals representing the bits travel down a single wire in "single file." Most serial transmission systems use pulses to represent the bits. A serially transmitted binary number might look like an irregular train of pulses: a pulse appearing for every 1 bit, and a void appearing for every 0 bit. "Feet first" is the usual procedure, with the least significant bit (2^0) leading the train of pulses.

Serial transmission is simpler than parallel transmission, but it is much slower. The choice of method depends on the desired performance versus the cost and complexity of the computer being designed.

THE FIVE CIRCUIT "BUILDING BLOCKS"

The five basic circuits listed earlier in this chapter are often called "building blocks," for they are arranged in various combinations to build the calculating and control sections of a digital computer. The following paragraphs will briefly describe the properties and functions of these building blocks. Their actual circuitry will be discussed in the next chapter.

The *bistable circuit* is a circuit that has two recognizable stable operating states or conditions. A switch, for example, is a bistable device: its two stable states are "on" and "off." Bistable circuits are used to represent the bits within the calculating sections of a computer. One of the two stable states is assigned to represent 1, and the other represents 0. Several bistable circuits are normally grouped together to represent whole binary numbers, each circuit corresponding to one digit of the number. Bistable circuits enable a computer to hold information temporarily while it is being processed in much the same way that we write down numbers on a piece of paper when we work an arithmetic problem.

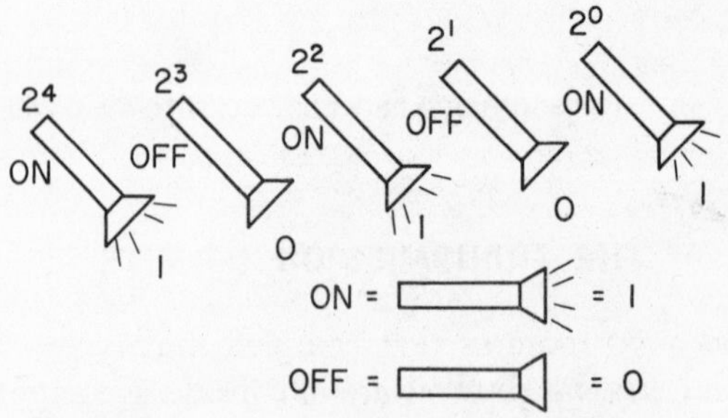

FIG. 4-3. A flashlight is a familiar "bistable element." These five flashlights represent the binary number 10101.

Picture a row of five flashlights. A flashlight is a bistable device since it is either "on" or "off." Let's represent 1 with "on" and 0 with "off." In this fashion, this row of five flashlights can represent any binary number between 00000 and 11111. Binary 10101, for example, would be represented by turning the first, third, and fifth flashlights "on," and leaving the second and fourth flashlights "off."

The word "gate" suggests some kind of forceful control, and, in fact, *AND gates* and *OR gates* actively route the flow of bits through a computer. Their action is somewhat similar to railroad switches that control the movement of trains along a network of tracks. By opening and closing selected switches, the train controller can route a particular train to any desired station. In a digital computer, to finish the comparison, groups of gates working together are able to send particular bits of information to specified locations.

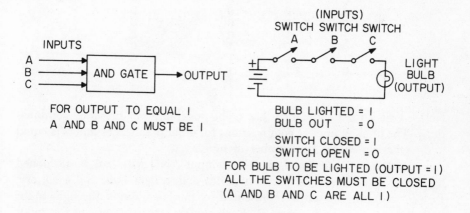

FIG. 4-4.   A simple AND gate model.

The easiest way to understand the operation of a gate is to picture it as a black box (a small one this time!) that has a single *output terminal* and more than one *control terminal.* Gates can be built with any number of control terminals, but few computer applications require more than five or six.

If we were to feed electrical signals representing bits into the control terminals, we would observe that an electrical signal appears at the output terminal. We would also find that the value of the output bit (0 or 1) is "functionally related" to the values of the input bits. Simply stated, this means that a gate will generate a 1 bit at its ouput terminal only if bits of correct values have been fed into the control terminals.

The control terminals are usually called *inputs,* although this name can be somewhat misleading. In most gate circuits the "input" bits (control bits) do not "pass through the gate" to produce the output; they function as a control of the value of the output bit. However, for purposes of simplification, we will call the control terminals "inputs."

AND gates and OR gates differ in the correct values of input bits that will cause a 1 output. An AND gate will generate a 1 output only if *all* of the inputs are 1 bits.

A convenient way of picturing the operation of digital computer circuits that is especially useful for gates is to construct a table that lists all of the possible input bit-value combinations, and the resulting output for each combination. An *input-output relationship table* for a three-input AND gate is shown below. The inputs are labeled A, B and C.

INPUTS			OUTPUT
A	B	C	
0	0	0	0
1	0	0	0
0	1	0	0
1	1	0	0
0	0	1	0
1	0	1	0
0	1	1	0
1	1	1	1

Notice that a three-input gate has eight possible input bit-value combinations. The total number of combinations for other numbers of inputs is equal to 2^n, where n equals the number of inputs.

A simple electrical model of a three-input AND gate can be fashioned by wiring three "on-off" switches in *series* with a light bulb and a battery. In this model the output is represented by the condition of the light bulb: bulb lighted = 1; bulb out = 0. Each switch represents one of the input bits: "on" = 1; "off" = 0.

Obviously, the output will be 1 (bulb lighted) only when all three switches are "on" (all inputs equal 1).

The OR gate, on the other hand, generates a 1 bit output if *any* of the input bits equals 1. The input-output relationship table for a three-input OR gate is shown below. The inputs are labeled X, Y and Z.

INPUTS			OUTPUT
X	Y	Z	
0	0	0	0
1	0	0	1
0	1	0	1
1	1	0	1
0	0	1	1
1	0	1	1
0	1	1	1
1	1	1	1

The simple electrical model for this three-input OR gate consists of a bank of three parallel switches wired in series with a light bulb and battery. In this circuit the bulb will light (output equals 1) if any of the three switches are "on" (any of the inputs equals 1).

It is left as an exercise for the reader to show that if the output symbols are interchanged so that bulb lighted = 0 and bulb out = 1, the AND gate model now represents an OR gate, and the OR gate model now represents an AND gate.

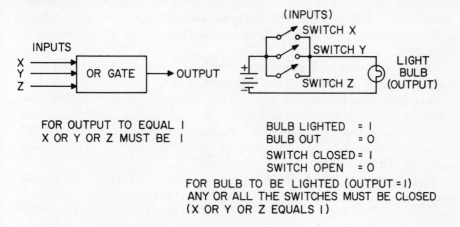

FOR OUTPUT TO EQUAL 1
X OR Y OR Z MUST BE 1

BULB LIGHTED   = 1
BULB OUT   = 0
SWITCH CLOSED = 1
SWITCH OPEN   = 0
FOR BULB TO BE LIGHTED (OUTPUT = 1)
ANY OR ALL THE SWITCHES MUST BE CLOSED
(X OR Y OR Z EQUALS 1)

FIG. 4-5.   A simple OR gate model.

Summing up: an AND gate produces a 1 output only if *all* the inputs equal 1; an OR gate produces a 1 output if *any* of the inputs equals 1.

A *delay* circuit "slows down" the movement of electrical signals representing bits. As we shall see later, it is often important that one bit reaches some circuit ahead of another bit. A delay placed in the path of the second bit will make certain that they arrive in the proper sequence.

The *inverter* is another black box, this one having only one input terminal and one output terminal. An inverter generates an output bit that is the *inverse* or "1's complement" of the input bit. If the input is 1, the output will be 0; if the input is 0 the output will be 1, as shown in the following input-out relationship table:

Input $= X$	Output $= \overline{X}$
0	1
1	0

Notice that the input bit has been labeled X, and the output bit has been labeled $\overline{X}$. $\overline{X}$ is read as "the inverse of X," the "complement of X" or "not

X." The last term arises from symbolic logic. If a logical statement is true, its inverse is "not true"; if the statement is false, its inverse is "not false." As a result, the inverter is often referred to as the NOT circuit.

LOGIC AND COMPUTERS

Now that we have discussed the functions and properties of the five basic building block circuits, we can investigate the manner in which they are grouped together to make up a digital computing system. The overall plan or scheme behind the arrangement of the building blocks is called the *logic* or *logical design* of a digital computer. A computer's logical design determines how it will do arithmetic, interpret instructions, manipulate numbers and, in general, perform the functions associated with digital computer operation.

The "logic" in logical design refers to the branch of philosophy of the same name. Logic is the key to digital computer design.

Well over two thousand years ago, the Greek philosopher Aristotle invented a system of logic that he hoped would be useful in investigating the thinking and reasoning processes of the human mind. In the philosophical meaning of the word, logic is the study of the validity, or truth, of deductions made by the human mind.

Aristotle treated the thinking process as a chain of individual logical steps leading from some original statements to a final conclusion. The truth or falsity of the final conclusion depended on the truth or falsity of the simple statements the mind combined to come up with the conclusion. Aristotle tried to reconstruct the chain of thought and thereby build a word model of the thinking process. He ultimately hoped to be able to check the results of thinking by duplicating, step by step in words, the processes occuring in the mind.

Aristotle's system of logic is very fundamental because he considered all statements to be either true or false; no half truths or partial falsehoods are allowed. The results of his labors is a group of definitions and relationships. The definitions specify the type of statements that are permissible, and the relationships specify how they can be combined. With them, simple true-or-false statements can be combined into complicated valid expressions and the validity of existing expressions can be determined.

In 1847, George Boole, an English philosopher, took Aristotle's concepts and relationships and constructed a "logical algebra" based on them. In this algebra the elementary operations in the reasoning process are represented by symbols. Boole substituted algebraic symbols (a, b, c, etc.) for the simple written statements and defined a *new* set of algebraic operations to represent the logical combination relationships. Thus, a written logical expression can be represented by a *symbolically logical* equation, and these equations can be manipulated using *Boolean algebra*. The net effect is to make it possible to "solve" problems in logic by a Boolean algebraic "calculation."

Boolean algebra was considered an interesting but useless mathematical novelty until 1938. In that year, Claude E. Shannon of the Massachusetts Institute of Technology proved that symbolic logic could be used to represent switching circuits. He showed that two-state switches (either "on" or "off") can be symbolized with the same notation used to represent Aristotle's simple two-value (either true or false) logical statements.

Because of the switch-like nature of digital computer components, Boolean algebra has been adopted as a powerful aid to designing computer circuitry. First, the desired properties of a circuit are stated in an input-output relationship table. Then, the table is translated into a Boolean algebraic equation which represents the circuit. Finally, the equation is "solved" to determine the circuit having the desired properties.

INTRODUCTION TO LOGICAL DESIGN

Boolean algebra is a convenient and powerful tool for developing the logic of a digital computer. Strictly speaking, though, successful logical design can be performed without it, although the resulting computer system is likely to be more complicated than necessary. The reason for this is that Boolean algebraic equations, like ordinary algebraic equations, can often be *simplified*. This means that the circuit derived from the equation will require fewer building blocks than the equation implies. We will consider Boolean algebraic equations and discuss how to simplify them in the next section.

To help us appreciate the value of Boolean algebra, and better understand the meaning of logical design, let's design a very simple but important digital circuit the "hard way." Later, after we know more about symbolic logic, we will review the design and see how efficient it is.

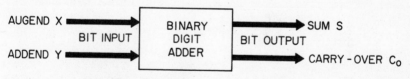

FIG. 4-6.   The "black box" binary digit adder.

A fundamental digital computer circuit is an *adder* capable of adding two binary digits together and producing a *sum bit* and a *carry-over bit*. How can we arrange the five building blocks to build an adder circuit? To find out, we must first look back at binary addition, and decide what the circuit must do. In other words, we must specify the desired properties of the adder circuit.

As we saw in Chapter 3, the rules governing binary arithmetic can be condensed into four simple tables. These rules apply to binary arithmetic in general, not just to pencil-and-paper calculations. The arithmetic section of a digital computer, and the circuits it is made up of, must also obey them. This means that the adder must perform the operations listed in the binary addition table:

(augend bits)	0	0	1	1
(addend bits)	+ 0	+ 1	+ 0	+ 1
(sum bits)	0	1	1	0	plus a carry-over bit of 1

A quick look at the table shows that the adder circuit must have two input terminals and two output terminals.

The two bits to be added (remember that we are dealing with electrical signals that represent the bits) are fed into the inputs. For convenience we will label the augend bit X and the addend bit Y. The corresponding inputs will be called the X input and Y input, respectively.

The two outputs produced by the adder circuit are the sum bit, which we will call S, the the carry-over bit, C_o. The C_o bit equals 1 whenever both X and Y equal 1.

The table shown above lists the four possible combinations of two binary digits that can be added together, along with the sum and carry-over digits resulting from each combination. The adder circuit must produce the sum and carry-over bits called for by the table when the corresponding combination of input bits is applied. The following input-output relationship table completely specifies the properties of the adder circuit:

INPUTS		OUTPUTS	
X	Y	C_o	S
0	0	0	0
1	0	0	1
0	1	0	1
1	1	1	0

Our problem, therefore, is to figure out a building block arrangement that has the input-output relationship shown in the above table.

If we were using symbolic logic and Boolean algebra we could derive a logical equation based on the table and quickly convert it to an arrangement of building blocks. This is possible because an input-output relationship table is really a "longhand" way of writing the symbolic logic equation that represents the circuit.

Now, though, we will use the direct approach. This consists of looking closely at the table, seeing what it says, and reasoning out a building block arrangement having the specified properties.

The input-output relationship table indicates that the S bit must equal

1 when either $X = 1$ and $Y = 0$; or $X = 0$ and $Y = 1$. The word "either" gives us an important clue; it suggests that the output terminal of the adder is actually the output terminal of a two-input OR gate. The inputs to this OR gate represent the input conditions $X = 1$ and $Y = 0$; $X = 0$ and $Y = 1$.

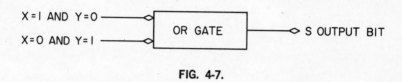

FIG. 4-7.

The output of a two-input OR gate will be 1 when either of its input bits is 1. Our next step, therefore, is to design two circuits that will be connected to the inputs of the OR gate. One of the circuits will generate a 1 bit when $X = 1$ and $Y = 0$; the other will generate a 1 bit when $X = 0$ and $Y = 1$.

The "ands" in the input combinations tell us that each circuit will contain an AND gate. But, as we know, the output of an AND gate equals 1 only when all of the input bits equal 1. We want the output to be 1 when one of the inputs equals 0.

We can solve this problem with the help of two inverter building blocks. The output of an inverter is the inverse or complement of the input. That is, if the input equals 0 the output will equal 1.

Consider the first input combination, $X = 1$ and $Y = 0$. A little thought will verify that an equivalent expression is $X = 1$ and $\overline{Y} = 1$. Since $Y = 0$, the inverse of Y, or $\overline{Y}$, equals 1. We can use an inverter to turn Y into $\overline{Y}$, and then feed this into an AND gate along with X, as shown in Fig. 4-8. As the input-output relationship table shows, this arrangement does indeed produce a 1 when $X = 1$ and $Y = 0$.

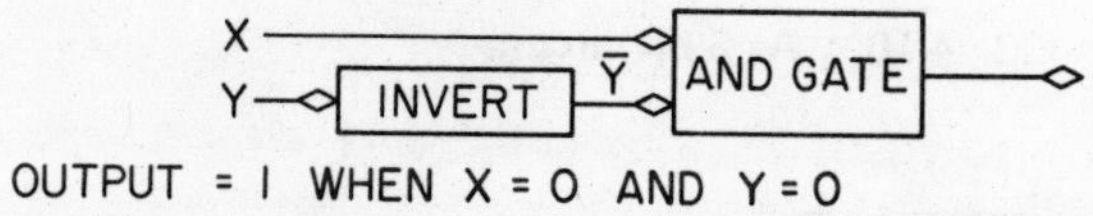

X ——————
Y —◁[INVERT]$\overline{Y}$[AND GATE]—◇

OUTPUT = 1 WHEN X = 0 AND Y = 0

X	Y	OUTPUT
0	0	0
1	0	1
0	1	0
1	1	0

FIG. 4-8.

The second input combination is a "mirror image" of the first. A building block arrangement that will produce a 1 output when $X = 0$ and $Y = 1$ is shown in Fig. 4-9. This circuit corresponds to the relationship where output equals 1 when $\overline{X} = 1$ and $Y = 1$.

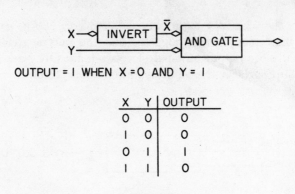

OUTPUT = I WHEN X = 0 AND Y = I

X	Y	OUTPUT
0	0	0
I	0	0
0	I	I
I	I	0

FIG. 4-9.

By combining these two AND gate circuits with the OR gate we discussed earlier, we have the circuit shown in Fig. 4-10. This building block arrangement generates a 1 bit output whenever $X = 1$ and $Y = 0$ *or* $X = 0$ and $Y = 1$. The reader should check the input-output relationship table shown by tracing the path of various X and Y bit combinations through the circuit.

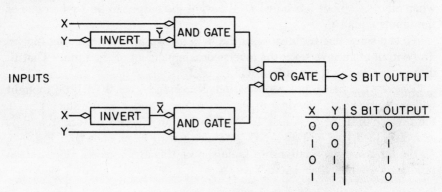

X	Y	S BIT OUTPUT
0	0	0
I	0	I
0	I	I
I	I	0

FIG. 4-10.   An S bit circuit.

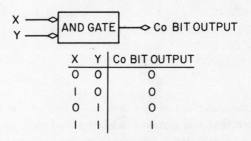

X	Y	Co BIT OUTPUT
0	0	0
I	0	0
0	I	0
I	I	I

FIG. 4-11.   A Co bit circuit.

So much for the S bit; now for the carry-over bit, C_o. There is no problem here at all! The only combination of input bits that produces a C_o bit equal to 1 is $X = 1$ and $Y = 1$. A single two-input AND gate is all that's necessary to implement this expression, as shown in Fig. 4-11.

The complete adder circuit is shown in Fig. 4-12.

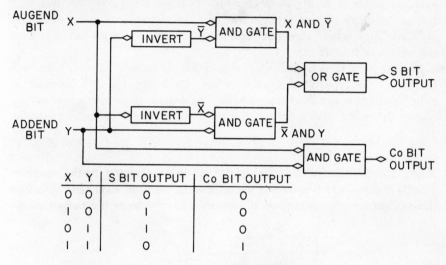

FIG. 4-12.   A binary digit adder circuit.

This simple example of logical design was intended to illustrate two important points:

1. Binary arithmetic can be performed by circuits made up of the basic building blocks. Numbers are groups of digits, so it follows that if single circuits can work with single pairs of digits, several circuits can be combined to work with whole binary numbers.
2. The essence of logical design is first to specify completely the properties a circuit must have, and then "work backwards" to develop a building block circuit having these properties.

We really used a trial-and-error method to develop the adder circuit. It's easy to see that a more convenient technique is called for; one that enables a designer to build up computer circuitry in a straightforward and efficient manner. As we shall see, Boolean algebra is the key to effective computer circuit design.

BOOLEAN ALGEBRA

In 1854, George Boole published a book entitled *An Investigation of the Laws of Thought,* in which he described his symbolic logic notation, and the logical algebra that has since become known as Boolean algebra.

Boole based his logical notation on Aristotle's system of logic, which deals with statements that are either completely true or completely false. He assigned true statements a value of 1, and false statements a value of 0. These two numbers are the only values that are allowed in Boolean algebra. The variables and constants in a Boolean algebraic equation must have a value of either 0 or 1. Keep this fact in mind whenever we deal with Boolean algebra. Even though the equations may look very similar to ordinary "high school algebraic" equations, the various terms can only have the values of 0 or 1.

Boolean algebra is best illustrated with simple switch, battery, light bulb circuits of the type we discussed earlier. Each variable in a Boolean algebraic equation can be represented by one switch; the whole equation represents the entire switch circuit. For example, a typical equation might be:

$$X + Y = L$$

X and Y both represent switches in the circuit represented by the equation. The "+" sign (which does not mean plus, as we shall soon see) tells how the switches are connected in the circuit. L represents the output of 'the

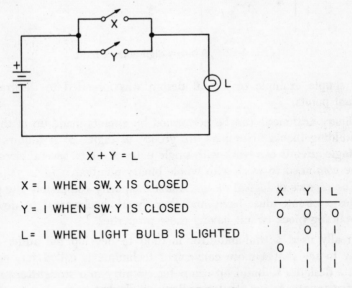

X + Y = L

X = I WHEN SW. X IS CLOSED

Y = I WHEN SW. Y IS CLOSED

L = I WHEN LIGHT BULB IS LIGHTED

X	Y	L
0	0	0
I	0	I
0	I	I
I	I	I

FIG. 4-13.   The OR function.

circuit, which in this case will be the condition of the light bulb. X and Y will have values of 1 when the switches they represent are "on"; they will have values of 0 when their corresponding switch is "off." L will have a value of 1 when the light bulb is lighted, and a value of 0 when the light bulb is not lighted.

THE OR FUNCTION

Boolean algebra enables us to represent switching circuits with simple equations. The interconnections of the individual switches are represented by *logical functions*. These logical functions are analogous in *purpose* to the arithmetic operations in algebraic equations, although they are totally different in their meaning.

The first logical function is the *OR function*. If two switches, X and Y, are connected in parallel together with a battery and light bulb, as shown in Fig. 4-13, the bulb will light if either of the switches is "on." The Boolean algebraic equation for this circuit is:

$$X + Y = L$$

In this equation the "+" sign means OR; the equation is read as "X *or* Y equals L." Notice that this equation represents the operation of a two-input OR gate. The OR gate is a circuit that performs the logical OR function.

The logical OR function, as well as the other logical functions, is often pictured in a tabular form called a *truth table*. The OR function truth table is shown below:

X + Y = L	X	Y	L
(X or Y equals L)	0	0	0
	1	0	1
	0	1	1
	1	1	1

As we might expect, this truth table is identical to the input-output relationship table for a two-input OR gate. However, "input and output" refers only to building block terminals, not to algebraic expressions. Therefore, we shall call Boolean algebraic tables "truth tables," and save input-output for circuit use.

The OR function can be extended to any number of variables. This means that any number of switches can be added on, in parallel to X and Y. For example, a third switch, Z, added in parallel would change the equation to:

$$X + Y + Z = L$$
$$(X \text{ or } Y \text{ or } Z \text{ equals } L)$$

The truth table for this equation is identical to the input-output relationship table for the three-input OR gate we discussed earlier.

Two important laws that can be used to simplify logical equations are the *associative* and *commutative* laws for the OR function. These are:

Commutative Law: $X + Y = Y + X$
Associative Law: $(X + Y) + Z = X + (Y + Z) = X + Y + Z$

These laws are easily verified by drawing the switching circuits they represent, as shown in Fig. 4-14.

COMMUTATIVE LAW
X + Y = Y + X

ASSOCIATIVE LAW
(X+Y)+Z = X + (Y+Z) = X+Y+Z

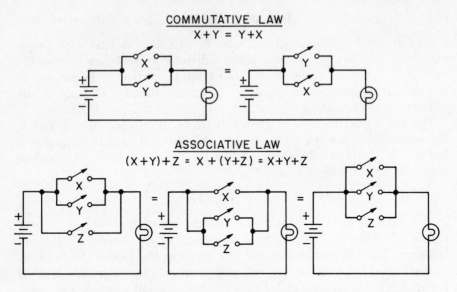

FIG. 4-14.   Commutative and Associative Laws for the OR function.

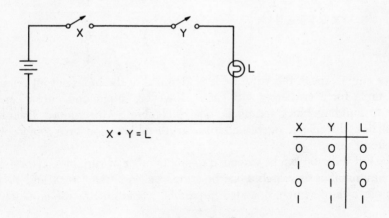

X • Y = L

X	Y	L
0	0	0
1	0	0
0	1	0
1	1	1

FIG. 4-15.   The AND function.

THE AND FUNCTION

Connecting two switches, X and Y, in series with a battery and light bulb, as shown in Fig. 4-15, produces a circuit represented by the AND function. The bulb will light only if both A *and* B are "on." The Boolean equation is:

$$X \cdot Y = L$$
(X and Y equals L)

The "·" means *and*. It is apparent that the AND gate building block performs the logical AND function. The AND function, too, can be extended to any number of variables. This means that additional switches are added in series with X and Y. With a third switch, Z, the equation becomes:

$$X \cdot Y \cdot Z = L$$
(X and Y and Z equals L)

The commutative and associative laws also apply to the AND function:

Commutative law: $X \cdot Y = Y \cdot X$
Associative law: $X \cdot (Y \cdot Z) = (X \cdot Y) \cdot Z = X \cdot Y \cdot Z$

These laws may be verified by drawing the switch circuits they represent, as shown in Fig. 4-16.

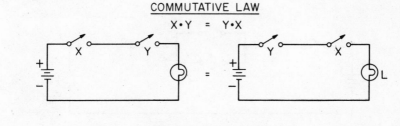

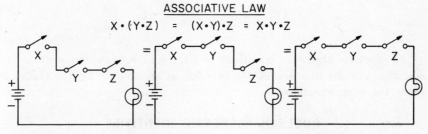

FIG. 4-16.   Commutative and Associative Laws for the AND function.

MORE SWITCH CIRCUITS

The AND and OR functions are the basic Boolean algebraic operations. We have seen how these functions can be used to represent simple switching circuits. Most useful Boolean equations, however, contain both AND and OR functions. These equations are a bit more complicated to deal with, although they are fundamentally the same as single-function equations. For example, a typical Boolean equation and its corresponding truth table are:

A · (B + C) = L	A	B	C	(B + C)	A · (B + C) = L
(A and B or C equals L)	0	0	0	0	0
	1	0	0	0	0
	0	1	0	1	0
	1	1	0	1	1
	0	0	1	1	0
	1	0	1	1	1
	0	1	1	1	0
	1	1	1	1	1

Notice that the truth table contains the intermediate relationship $(B + C)$, as well as the variables A, B and C. Writing this table is a two-step operation. First, the possible values of $(B + C)$ that correspond to the various combinations of B and C must be found. Then, the possible values of L can be determined by considering $A \cdot (B + C)$.

The circuit represented by this equation is shown in Fig. 4-17.

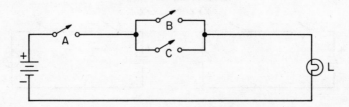

FIG. 4-17.   A · (B + C) = L.

The Boolean algebraic equations in Fig. 4-18 are written next to the switching circuits they represent. It is left as an exercise for the reader to verify the representation.

BOOLEAN ALGEBRAIC IDENTITIES

Several identities, or basic relationships, exist in Boolean algebra that are very useful in simplifying symbolic logic equations. A few of the more important ones are shown in Fig. 4-19 below the switching circuits they represent. Their validity is readily apparent.

THE NOT (OR INVERSE) FUNCTION

The inverter building block complements, or inverts, a binary digit. In Boolean terminology this operation is called complementation or *negation*, and is represented as follows:

$$\overline{1} = 0 \quad \text{(NOT 1 equals 0)}$$
$$\overline{0} = 1 \quad \text{(NOT 0 equals 1)}$$

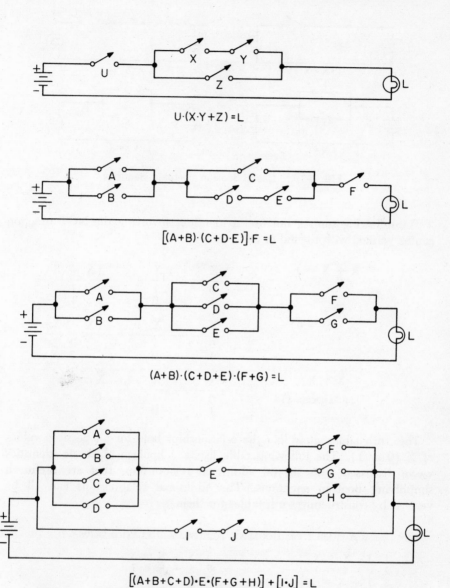

$$U \cdot (X \cdot Y + Z) = L$$

$$[(A+B) \cdot (C+D \cdot E)] \cdot F = L$$

$$(A+B) \cdot (C+D+E) \cdot (F+G) = L$$

$$[(A+B+C+D) \cdot E \cdot (F+G+H)] + [I \cdot J] = L$$

FIG. 4-18.   Some logical equations and their corresponding switching circuits.

Notice that a line drawn above a symbol indicates that the symbol's inverse is to be taken. Therefore:

if $X = 1$, then $\overline{X} = 0$

if $X = 0$, then $\overline{X} = 1$

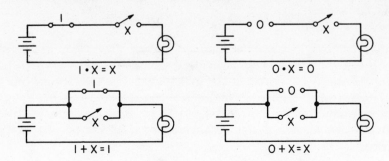

FIG. 4-19.   Useful Boolean algebraic identities.

The following simple, but useful identities involving the NOT function can be verified with the aid of truth tables:

X	$\overline{X}$	$(X + \overline{X})$
0	1	1
1	0	1

$X + \overline{X} = 1$

X	$\overline{X}$	$(X \cdot \overline{X})$
0	1	0
1	0	0

$X \cdot \overline{X} = 0$

X	$\overline{X}$	$\overline{\overline{X}}$
0	1	0
1	0	1

$\overline{\overline{X}} = X$
(Double negation)

The truth tables show that the relationships hold for all possible values of X (0 or 1). The following table lists the Boolean algebraic identities we've discussed, plus several additional relationships that are useful in simplifying Boolean equations. The additional relationships can all be verified by constructing truth tables for them.

A TABLE OF BOOLEAN ALGEBRAIC RELATIONSHIPS

1. $1 \cdot X = X$
2. $0 \cdot X = 0$
3. $1 + X = 1$
4. $0 + X = X$
5. $X + X = X$
6. $X + \overline{X} = 1$
7. $X \cdot \overline{X} = 0$
8. $\overline{\overline{X}} = X$
9. $X \cdot (Y + Z) = X \cdot Y + X \cdot Z$
10. $X \cdot (X + Y) = X$
11. $X + (X \cdot Z) = X$
12. $(X + Y) \cdot (X + Z) = X + Y \cdot Z$
13. $X + \overline{X} \cdot Y = X + Y$
14. $X \cdot Y = Y \cdot X$
15. $X + Y = Y + X$ } Commutative Laws
16. $(X \cdot Y) \cdot Z = X \cdot (Y \cdot Z) = X \cdot Y \cdot Z$
17. $(X + Y) + Z = X + (Y + Z) = X + Y + Z$ } Associative Laws
18. $\overline{X + Y + Z} = \overline{X} \cdot \overline{Y} \cdot \overline{Z}$
19. $\overline{X \cdot Y \cdot Z} = \overline{X} + \overline{Y} + \overline{Z}$ } "De Morgan's Laws"

THE ADDER CIRCUIT IN REVIEW

Let's return to the problem of designing a binary digit adder, but this time we will tackle it with Boolean algebraic methods.

We will start by considering the input-output relationship table for the adder that we used before. Actually, it is two tables in one, since it gives the input-output relationships for both the S bit and the C_o bit. In order to apply Boolean algebra design techniques, each of the outputs must be described by its own table.

X	Y	S		X	Y	C_o
0	0	0		0	0	0
1	0	1		1	0	0
0	1	1		0	1	0
1	1	0		1	1	1

We must now find a method of deriving a Boolean equation that represents a correct circuit from the specified input-output relationships. In other words, we desire an equation that describes the properties of the adder circuit in symbolic logic terms.

This is a two step method:

1. An additional column is added to each input-output relationship table. This column lists "anded" terms — terms which are formed by "anding" (combining with the logical AND function) the symbols representing the input variables. There is a trick involved, however: if the input variable has a value of 0 in a particular row, the *complement* (inverse) of its symbol is used in the "anded" term in that row.

S Bit Table

INPUT VARIABLES		"ANDED" TERMS	OUTPUT
X	Y		S
0	0	$X \cdot Y$	0
1	0	$X \cdot Y$	1
0	1	$X \cdot Y$	1
1	1	$X \cdot Y$	0

C_o Bit Table

X	Y		C_o
0	0	$X \cdot Y$	0
1	0	$X \cdot Y$	0
0	1	$X \cdot Y$	0
1	1	$X \cdot Y$	1

2. Whenever an output, S or C_o, equals 1, the corresponding "anded"

term is removed from the table and written as a term in an "or'd" equation. These equations represent the desired circuit:

For S = 1
$$S = X \cdot \bar{Y} + \bar{X} \cdot Y$$

For C_0 = 1
$$C_0 = X \cdot Y$$

Notice that these equations are the Boolean algebraic equivalents of the "word descriptions" we used earlier:

"S equals 1 when X and not Y equals 1, or when not X and Y equals 1."

"C_0 equals 1 when X and Y equals 1."

Earlier, we used six building block circuits to construct the adder. You'll notice that the type and number of blocks used corresponds to the number and type of logical functions in the equations — three AND functions, two NOT functions and one OR function. The number of required building blocks can be reduced if the equations are simplified:

For S = 1
$$S = (X + Y) \cdot (\overline{X \cdot Y})$$

For C_0 = 1
$$C_0 = X \cdot Y$$

The reader should verify with the aid of a truth table that the simplified and the original equations are functionally equivalent. Simplifying the equation reduces the required number of building blocks to four. A fifty per cent savings on circuit components is a considerable one when hundreds of identical units might be required.

The new adder circuit is shown in Fig. 4-20.

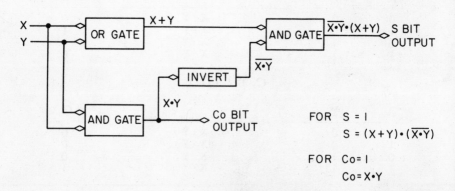

FIG. 4-20.   A simplified binary digit adder circuit.

We will say more about the techniques of going from a Boolean equation to a circuit diagram in Chapter 6. It's clear, though, that the equation is "talked through." Every building block in the circuit corresponds to one of the logical functions in the equation.

REVIEW QUESTIONS

1. Explain how the two binary digits may be represented by electrical signals.
2. Describe the functions of the five basic computer "building blocks."
3. Explain the meaning of "logical design."
4. Draw an input-output relationship table and design a simple switch, light bulb, battery model for a 4-input AND gate; a 4-input OR gate.
5. Explain the similarities and differences between an input-output relationship table and a "truth table."
6. Draw simple switch, light bulb, battery models represented by the following logical expressions:

$$(A \cdot B) + (C \cdot D) + (E \cdot F) \quad = L$$
$$(A \cdot B + C) \cdot (D + E) \quad\quad\quad = L$$
$$(A \cdot B \cdot C \cdot D) + (E + F) \cdot G = L$$

7. Using truth tables, prove De Morgan's Laws (page 60).
8. Explain the procedure used to derive a Boolean equation that represents a desired circuit from the input-output relationship table for the circuit.
9. Verify that the binary digit adder circuit derived with the aid of Boolean algebra has the same properties as the circuit derived by the "direct approach."

5—Building Block Circuits

In this chapter we shall discuss the electronic circuits used in the five basic digital computer building blocks. Simply speaking, these are circuits that have the input-output relationships of the "black boxes" we looked at earlier.

Digital computer circuits can be divided into the following groups:

1. Circuits that perform logical operations on input signals, including the AND gate and the OR gate. As we have seen, there are many ways to represent binary digits with electrical signals. One voltage level can stand for 1, for example, and another voltage level for 0; or the presence of a pulse may denote 1, and the absence of a pulse, 0. The output signal of a logical circuit, then, represents the "result" of a logical operation performed on the input signals.
2. Bistable circuits, such as the *flip-flop*, which store binary digits (bits). Here again, electrical signals symbolize the storage operation. An input signal "sets" the bistable circuit to one of its two stable states; output signals indicate which state the circuit is in.
3. Counting circuits that can count the number of bits fed into an input. Bits to be counted are represented by electrical signals, as is the total count contained in the circuit.
4. Delay circuits, whose output signal is an exact copy of the input signal, generated some time after the input was applied.
5. Auxiliary circuitry that is necessary for the operation of the above circuits or improves their performance. Examples of auxiliary circuits are power supplies, waveform restorers, display devices, etc. We will not discuss this group of circuits.

The majority of modern electronic computers are built of circuitry containing vacuum tubes, transistors and diodes operating as two-state switches.

Before discussing the actual circuits, let's investigate the switching characteristics of these devices.

An ideal switch offers zero resistance when it is "closed," or "on," and infinite resistance when it is "open," or "off." Electron tubes and semiconductor devices can be used as switches, although they don't have these ideal characteristics. Relays and other electro-mechanical switches come closer to the ideal, but they operate much too slowly for high-speed computer applications. The advantages of an "electronic switch" are its high speed operation, relatively small size (depending on the type of device) and long life, as it has no moving parts.

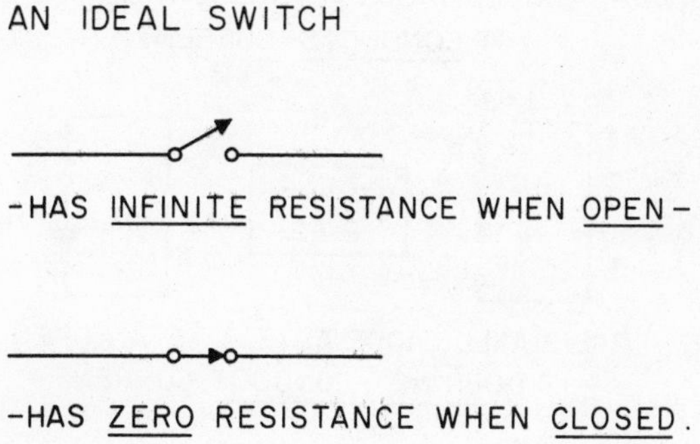

AN IDEAL SWITCH

-HAS <u>INFINITE</u> RESISTANCE WHEN <u>OPEN</u> -

-HAS <u>ZERO</u> RESISTANCE WHEN <u>CLOSED</u>.

FIG. 5-1.   An ideal switch has these characteristics.

DIODES

A *vacuum diode* will permit current to flow through it in only one direction. A heated cathode within the tube emits electrons. If the anode (or plate) is made positive with respect to the cathode, electrons will be attracted to the anode, and a current will flow. If, on the other hand, the anode is made negative with respect to the cathode, electrons will be repelled back to the cathode, and no current will flow.

Thus, depending on the polarity of the anode to cathode voltage, a vacuum diode will act as a closed, or "on," switch, or an open, or "off," switch. When the tube is conducting it has a resistance of about 2000 ohms; when not conducting, it may, for all practical purposes, be considered an open circuit (infinite resistance).

Semiconductor diodes display similar switching characteristics. When the diode is "forward biased" it conducts current, acting as a resistance of about 50 ohms or less. When "back biased" it has a small "leakage current."

When used as a switch, the important characteristics of any diode are its "on" resistance, "off" resistance and the length of time required to switch from one state to the other.

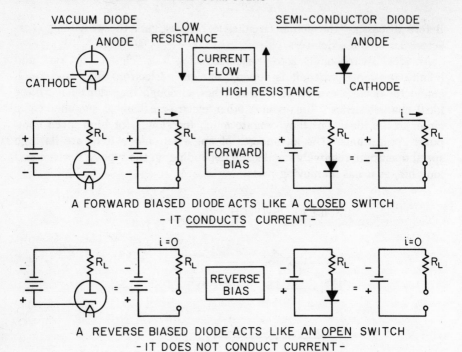

FIG. 5-2. Diode action.

TRIODES

A vacuum triode is similar in construction to a vacuum diode, except that an additional electrode, the control grid, is placed between the anode and cathode. The grid can control the flow of electrons between the cathode and anode. In normal triode operation, the anode is made positive with respect to the cathode, so that electrons emitted by the cathode will be attracted to the anode, allowing a current to flow through the tube. If the grid is now made slightly negative, some of the electrons leaving the cathode will be repelled back to it. More electrons will be repelled as the grid is made more negative. If the grid is set to 0 volts, or made slightly positive, electrons can move past it unhindered. Thus, the grid voltage can control the current flowing between the cathode and anode. Because of the grid's shape and position inside the tube, a small change in grid voltage causes a large change in the tube current. Hence, the triode can be used to amplify small signals.

When used as a switch, the triode is operated at the extreme ends of its characteristics: it is either "cut-off" or "saturated." At cut-off the grid voltage is sufficiently negative to completely stop the flow of electrons — the switch is "off." At the saturation point, the grid is set at 0 volts, or made slightly positive, and all the electrons emitted by the cathode reach the anode — the switch is "on." Cut-off is characterized by a very high anode to cathode resistance; saturation, by a low resistance.

The *semiconductor triode*, or *transistor*, is a current-controlled amplifying device. That is, the current flowing in one terminal controls the current flowing between the other two. Although the principles of operation of a transistor are quite different than those of a vacuum tube, it is possible to draw a rough analogy between the electrodes of a vacuum triode and the terminals of a transistor. The collector may be compared to the anode, the emitter to the cathode, and the base to the control grid. Readers are urged to consult the books listed in the bibliography to obtain a more complete picture of transistor theory.

The transistor logic circuits in this chapter all use n-p-n transistors. P-n-p transistor circuits are identical, except that all circuit polarities (supply voltages, input signals, etc.) are reversed.

When the base of a properly biased n-p-n transistor is made slightly positive with respect to the emitter, a small base-emitter current flows, which causes a much larger current flow between the collector and emitter. As the base voltage is increased, more current flows between collector and emitter, until the transistor saturates. Saturation is characterized by a very low collector to emitter resistance.

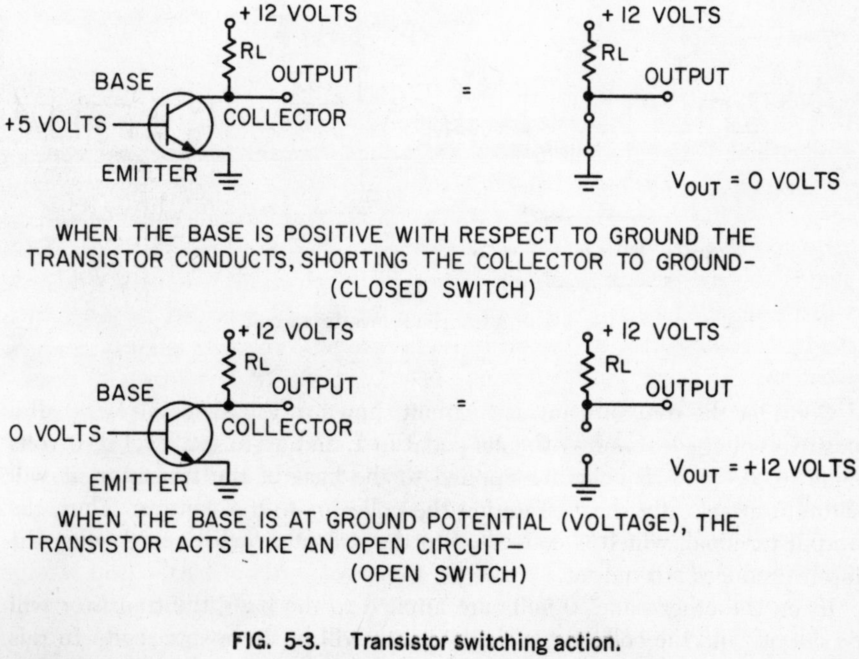

WHEN THE BASE IS POSITIVE WITH RESPECT TO GROUND THE
TRANSISTOR CONDUCTS, SHORTING THE COLLECTOR TO GROUND—
(CLOSED SWITCH)

WHEN THE BASE IS AT GROUND POTENTIAL (VOLTAGE), THE
TRANSISTOR ACTS LIKE AN OPEN CIRCUIT—
(OPEN SWITCH)

FIG. 5-3.   Transistor switching action.

If the base is made negative with respect to the emitter, the collector to emitter current is stopped, and the transistor is cut off. Cut-off is characterized by a very high collector to emitter resistance of several hundred thousand ohms.

CIRCUITS

A wide variety of electronic computer circuits have been developed. This chapter will make no attempt to discuss them all. Rather, the circuits presented are representative of many in use today. Semiconductor circuitry will be emphasized, since the transistor and semiconductor diode have virtually replaced vacuum tubes as computer switching elements.

Except for the various circuit voltages, semiconductor and vacuum diode circuits are basically the same. To avoid repetition, therefore, only semiconductor diode circuits will be discussed.

THE INVERTER

Transistor and vacuum triode switches are characterized by a phase inversion between input and output, and may therefore be used as logical inverters. That is, a 1 input produces a 0 output, and a 0 input produces a 1 output.

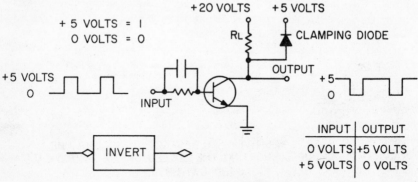

FIG. 5-4.   A transistor inverter circuit.

Consider the transistor inverter circuit shown in Fig. 5-4. We will call a positive voltage level of + 5 volts equal to 1, and a ground level of 0 volts equal to 0. If + 5 volts are applied to the base of the transistor, it will saturate, practically short-circuiting the collector to the emitter. Thus, the output terminal, which is connected to the collector, will be at 0 volts; a 1 input produces a 0 output.

If, on the other hand, 0 volts are applied to the base, the transistor will be cut off, and the collector to emitter path will be an open circuit. In this case, the output terminal will be +5 volts; a 0 input produces a 1 output.

The "clamping diode" on the collector load resistor serves to stabilize the collector voltage for different loadings on the inverter output, while the capacitor across the base resistor causes the transistor to switch more quickly when input levels change.

The equivalent vacuum triode inverter is shown in Fig. 5-5. Notice that the voltage levels representing 1 and 0 are different in this circuit. However, a "high" input produces a "low" output, and a "low" input produces a "high" output.

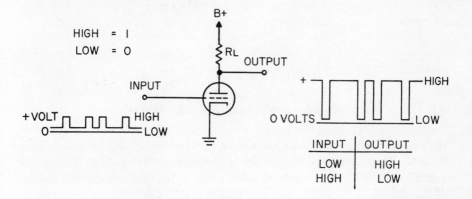

FIG. 5-5.   A vacuum triode inverter.

GATES

AND gates and OR gates are the basic logical circuits found in digital computers. The simplest gate circuits contain just diodes and resistors, and are called *diode logic* circuits, since the logical operations are performed by diodes.

A three-input diode logic AND gate is shown in Fig. 5-6. One diode is required for each input. The anodes of the three diodes are connected to a + 25 volt d-c power source through a common load resistor. As we have said, an AND gate will have a 1 output only if all the inputs equal 1.

The three inputs to the gate lead directly to the cathodes of the three diodes and can be either + 5 volts (representing 1), or 0 volts (representing 0). If we neglect the voltage drop across a diode when it is conducting, it is clear that the output terminal voltage is equal to the *lowest* voltage applied to any of its three inputs.

Since the power supply voltage is greater than the maximum possible input voltage (+5 volts), the diodes are always forward biased, and therefore always conducting current. However, forward biasing a diode only requires that the anode is made slightly more positive than the cathode. If

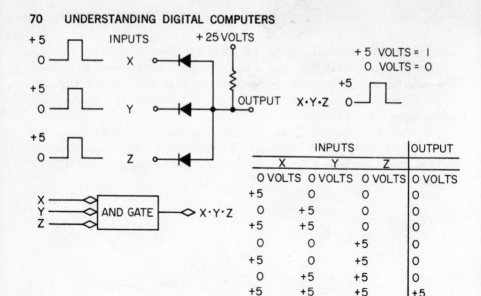

FIG. 5-6.   A three-input diode logic AND gate.

the cathode voltage is 0 volts, the anode voltage will be slightly greater than 0 volts. Thus, if any of the inputs to the diode AND gate is 0 volts, the output will be approximately 0 volts, since it is connected to the anodes of the diodes.

On the other hand, if all of the inputs to the AND gate (all the cathodes of the diodes) are at +5 volts, the anodes will be at a voltage slightly higher than +5 volts. Notice that all of the inputs must be at +5 volts for this to happen. Suppose that two of the inputs, X and Y, are equal to +5 volts, and the third input, Z, is at 0 volts. In this case, diode Z's anode will be at approximately 0 volts, which will "short-circuit" the other two anodes, making the output equal to 0 volts.

The above circuit can be made into an OR gate by reversing the diodes and the polarity of the power supply, as shown in Fig. 5-7. Arranged in this fashion, the diodes always conduct, because the cathodes are kept negative with respect to the anodes by the −25 volt power supply. A +5 volt signal applied to one of the inputs (one of the anodes) will cause a voltage of approximately +5 volts to appear at the corresponding cathode, and therefore at the output terminal. We see, then, that this circuit meets the requirements of an OR gate: the output equals 1 if any of the inputs equals 1.

Diode logic gates are simple, inexpensive and capable of high-speed operation. The problem of "loading" arises, however, if several diode gates are connected in series to develop a complicated logical expression. Simply stated, this means that the output signal of one gate is not strong enough to drive more than one or two inputs of other gates.

There are two common solutions to this problem. The first is to add amplifying stages to the gate outputs; the second is to use transistors or

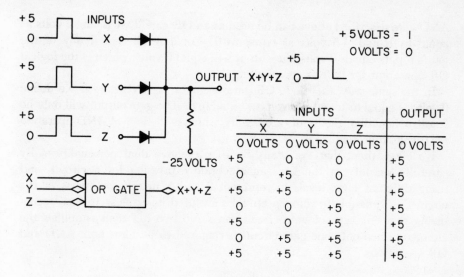

	INPUTS		OUTPUT
X	Y	Z	
0 VOLTS	0 VOLTS	0 VOLTS	0 VOLTS
+5	0	0	+5
0	+5	0	+5
+5	+5	0	+5
0	0	+5	+5
+5	0	+5	+5
0	+5	+5	+5
+5	+5	+5	+5

FIG. 5-7.   A three-input diode logic OR gate.

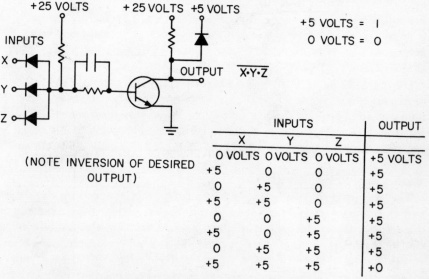

(NOTE INVERSION OF DESIRED OUTPUT)

	INPUTS		OUTPUT
X	Y	Z	
0 VOLTS	0 VOLTS	0 VOLTS	+5 VOLTS
+5	0	0	+5
0	+5	0	+5
+5	+5	0	+5
0	0	+5	+5
+5	0	+5	+5
0	+5	+5	+5
+5	+5	+5	+0

FIG. 5-8.   A diode-transistor logic AND gate.

vacuum tubes to perform the logical operations, since these devices provide built-in amplification.

The first approach is illustrated in Fig. 5-8. Notice that the gate output is inverted by the amplifying stage, for the transistor inverts the signal as it strengthens it. This isn't as serious as it sounds, for several reasons. First, there is no need to always represent 1's and 0's with the same logic levels throughout a large logic circuit. A little thought will verify that the diode

AND gate described above can be used as an OR gate if we define 0 volts as equal to 1, and +5 volts as equal to 0. You'll recall that if any of the gate's inputs equals 0 volts, the output will equal 0 volts, which is the logical OR operation for 0 volts representing 1.

In the same way, the diode OR gate becomes an AND gate if we define 0 volts as equal to 1, and +5 volts as equal to 0. The gate output will only be 0 volts when all of the inputs are 0 volts, which is the logical AND operation for 0 volts representing 1.

It's clear, then, that the basic diode gates have dual personalities. By carefully simplifying the Boolean algebraic expression for a circuit, and using different logic levels to represent 0 and 1 in different parts of the circuit, it is possible to compensate for unwanted inversions. In fact, recognizing that one type of gate circuit can serve two functions simplifies the circuitry, since only one gate circuit is required to perform both AND and OR operations.

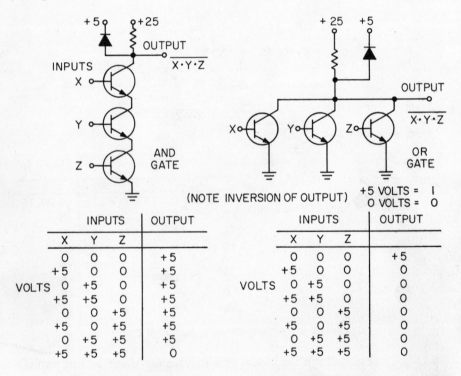

FIG. 5-9.   Direct-coupled transistor logic (DCTL) circuits.

Two examples of the second approach mentioned above, that of using transistors actually to perform logical operations, are illustrated in Fig. 5-9. DCTL, standing for direct-coupled transistor logic, is the name given to the two circuits shown: an AND gate and an OR gate. Here again, the output is the complement (inverse) of the desired result.

The output of the AND gate will be 0 volts only if the inputs to all three transistors are +5 volts. The transistors are in series, so they all must be saturated in order to ground the output terminal, setting it to 0 volts. If any input is 0 volts, the corresponding transistor will be cut off, and the output will be +5 volts.

Connecting three transistors in parallel produces a DCTL OR gate. If any of the inputs is at +5 volts, the corresponding transistor will be saturated, and the output voltage will be held at 0 volts. Only when all inputs are at 0 volts are the transistors cut off and the output equal to +5 volts.

DCTL circuits can be very small, require low power-supply voltages, and have very short switching times. However, they are expensive, since large numbers of transistors are required to perform complicated logic operations.

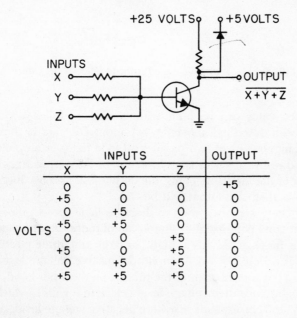

	INPUTS		OUTPUT
X	Y	Z	
0	0	0	+5
+5	0	0	0
0	+5	0	0
+5	+5	0	0
0	0	+5	0
+5	0	+5	0
0	+5	+5	0
+5	+5	+5	0

VOLTS

FIG. 5-10.   A resistor-transistor logic (RTL) circuit (NOR gate).

Resistor-transistor logic, abbreviated RTL, is similar to diode logic. Here, however, resistors, not diodes, are used to perform the logical operations. There is only one RTL circuit, often called the NOR gate, which is shown in Fig. 5-10. This circuit can be used either as an AND gate or as an OR gate depending on the logic levels chosen to represent 0 and 1. A +5 volt level applied to any of the inputs will saturate the transistor, setting the output voltage to 0 volts, regardless of the voltages of the other input signals.

Therefore, the circuit is an OR gate (with an inverted output) if +5 volts represents 1 and 0 volts represents 0; and the circuit is an AND gate if 0 volts represents 1 and +5 volts represents 0.

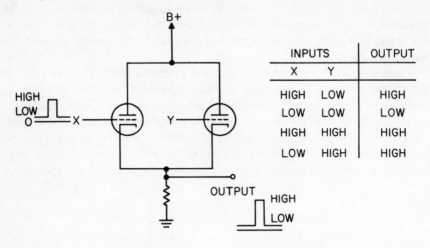

INPUTS		OUTPUT
X	Y	
HIGH	LOW	HIGH
LOW	LOW	LOW
HIGH	HIGH	HIGH
LOW	HIGH	HIGH

FIG. 5-11.   A direct-coupled cathode follower OR gate.

Vacuum tube gates can be built with triodes by following the direct-coupled approach described above. A two-input OR gate is shown in Fig. 5-11. The circuit consists of two parallel cathode follower amplifiers having a common load resistor. There is no inversion of the output signal with this gate. If either of the inputs is "high," the output will also be "high." If both inputs are "low" then the output will be "low."

"High" and "low" are often used to describe logic levels, since the levels often have the same polarity but different amplitudes. At the output of the triode OR gate, for example, 1 is a "high," or large amplitude positive voltage level, while 0 is a "low," or small amplitude positive voltage level. At each input terminal (the control grids of the tubes), on the other hand, 1 is represented by a slightly negative voltage level (close to 0 volts), which is called "high." "Low," or 0 corresponds to a more negative voltage level, sufficient to cut off the tubes.

The vacuum tube equivalent of the RTL NOR gate is illustrated in Fig. 5-12. This circuit uses a pentode tube, having three grid electrodes instead of one. The screen grid is connected to B+ (anode voltage), and the input signals are applied to the control and suppressor grids. This circuit produces an inverted output, and may be used both as an AND gate or as an OR gate.

Notice the input coupling capacitors. This circuit is suitable only for use with pulse signals that represent the bits. A positive pulse represents 1 and the absence of a pulse (no pulse) represents 0. A negative pulse will

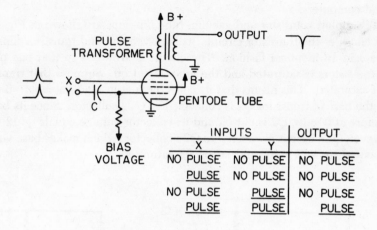

FIG. 5-12.   A pentode AND gate circuit.

appear at the output if positive pulses are applied to both inputs simultaneously. Thus, the circuit is an AND gate (with an inverted output) if a positive pulse represents 1, and an OR gate if a positive pulse represents 0.

BISTABLE CIRCUITS — THE FLIP-FLOP

A *flip-flop* is a bistable electronic circuit that is capable of storing one binary digit (bit). "Bistable" means that the circuit has two stable states or operating points. The name flip-flop results from the circuit's similarity to a toggle switch — it flips into one state and flops back into the other. One of these stable states can be used to represent 1, and the other used to represent 0. Thus, the value of a bit stored in a flip-flop is indicated by the state of the flip-flop.

The state representing 1 is commonly called *set*, and the state representing 0 is called *reset*.

From the standpoint of definition, any two-state circuit is a flip-flop, and there are many. Usually, though, the name refers to the *bistable multivibrator* developed by Eccles and Jordan in 1919. Its inventors had no particular application in mind when they built the first flip-flop (using vacuum tubes, of course). However, it soon found widespread use in pulse circuitry for radar, and was later used as the bistable element in ENIAC, the first high-speed electronic computer.

A *multivibrator* ("multi" for short) is a two-stage amplifier having "positive feedback." This means that the output of one amplifier stage is coupled to the input of the other amplifier stage, and vice versa. Depending on the coupling methods used, a multi can be bistable, monostable (one stable state) and astable (no stable states; it oscillates). All three are used in digital computers.

The simplest transistor and vacuum tube flip-flops are shown in Fig. 5-13. Let's consider the transistor circuits, as both vacuum and transistor flip-flops operate in an identical fashion. The circuit is arranged so that one of the two transistors is saturated and the other is cut off. Suppose that transistor Q1 is saturated. This means that its collector is at ground potential: 0 volts. But, the base of transistor Q2 is connected to Q1's collector. Since its base is therefore at 0 volts, Q2 is cut off and its collector voltage equals + 12 volts. However, Q1's base is connected to Q2's collector, which makes base voltage also equal to +12 volts, and keeps Q1 saturated.

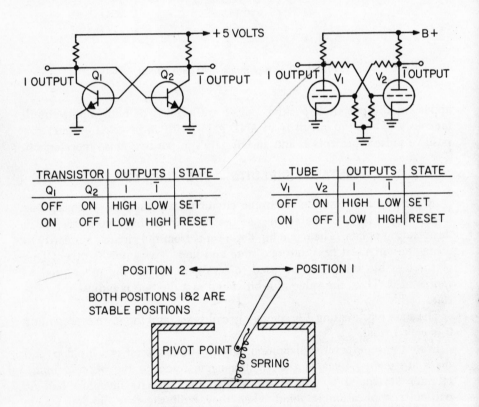

TRANSISTOR		OUTPUTS		STATE
Q_1	Q_2	I	$\bar{I}$	
OFF	ON	HIGH	LOW	SET
ON	OFF	LOW	HIGH	RESET

TUBE		OUTPUTS		STATE
V_1	V_2	I	$\bar{I}$	
OFF	ON	HIGH	LOW	SET
ON	OFF	LOW	HIGH	RESET

FIG. 5-13. (top) Basic flip-flop circuits. (bottom) A simple mechanical analogy of a flip-flop circuit.

The net result is somewhat like going around in a circle: Q1 is saturated, which keeps transistor Q2 cut off, which in turn keeps Q1 saturated, and on and on and on . . .

The second stable state — remember, there are two! — is identical to the one just described, except everything is "flipped." In this case Q1 is cut off and Q2 is saturated.

A transistor flip-flop that is more practical from the standpoint of reliability and high-speed operation is shown in Fig. 5-14. The capacitors that have been added increase switching speed by by-passing the coupling resistors when the flip-flop changes state.

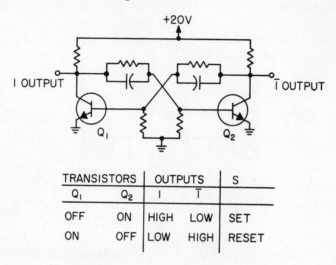

TRANSISTORS		OUTPUTS		S
Q_1	Q_2	I	$\bar{I}$	
OFF	ON	HIGH	LOW	SET
ON	OFF	LOW	HIGH	RESET

FIG. 5-14.   A transistor flip-flop circuit.

Notice that the circuit has two outputs: 1 and $\bar{1}$. When Q1 is cut off, its collector is at $+12$ volts, and so is the 1 output connected to it. At the same time, Q2 is saturated so that its collector and the $\bar{1}$ output are at 0 volts. To keep things simplified, we will call $+12$ volts "high" and 0 volts "low."

This condition (1 output "high" and $\bar{1}$ output "low") represents the SET state. That is, a flip-flop in this condition is storing a 1 bit.

If the circuit should "flip," cutting off Q2 and saturating Q1, the output potentials will interchange. The 1 output will be "low," and the $\bar{1}$ output will be "high." In this case, the flip-flop contains a 0 bit. This is the RESET state.

As we shall see in the next chapter, the complement output $\bar{1}$ is very handy, and can be used to simplify many complicated logic circuits.

FLIP-FLOP INPUTS

These simple flip-flops are missing a vital element: a means to *trigger* them to the desired state. In other words, we haven't provided any input terminals for the bit to be stored.

Most flip-flops have three inputs:

1. A SET input: applying a negative pulse to this input will trigger the flip-flop into the SET state.
2. A RESET input: applying a negative pulse to this input will trigger the flip-flop into the RESET state.
3. A COMPLEMENT input: applying a negative pulse to this input will cause the flip-flop to change states: SET will flip to RESET; or RESET will flop to SET.

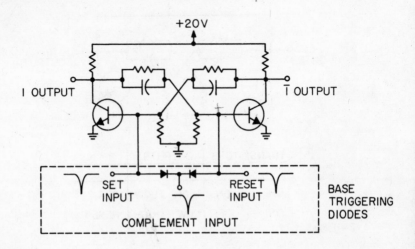

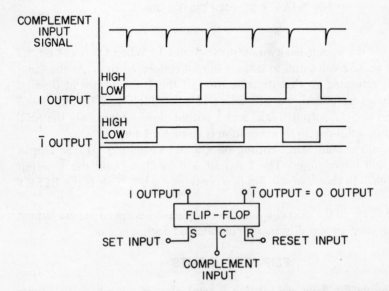

FIG. 5-15.   (top) A basic flip-flop circuit with triggering provisions—base triggering. (bottom) Circuit wave forms.

There are several ways to trigger a flip-flop. One often-used technique known as base triggering is shown in Fig. 5-15. In this circuit, diodes are used to "steer" the input signals to the transistor bases.

Suppose that the flip-flop is in the SET state (Q1 cut-off, Q2 saturated). A negative pulse applied to the RESET terminal is directed to the base of Q2, jolting it from its saturated state, and eventually causing it to cut off. In the process, the base voltage of Q1 increases from 0 volts, and it is driven into saturation.

A negative pulse applied to the COMPLEMENT input is steered by the diodes to the base of the saturated transistor, cutting it off, and changing the state of the flip-flop.

COUNTING CIRCUITS

Binary counting circuits are found throughout the control section of a digital computer. As you might expect, counting is a basic operation performed by a computer. Binary counters are circuits that count in the binary number system.

A simple "five-stage" binary counter is shown in Fig. 5-16. This circuit can count up to binary 11111 or $(31)_{10}$. It contains five flip-flops, one for each power of 2. Negative pulses to be counted are fed into the COMPLE-MENT input of F.F.0 (2^0 flip-flop). The $\bar{1}$ output of each flip-flop drives the COMPLEMENT input of the succeeding flip-flop.

Suppose the counter initially registers 00000. This means that all the flip-flops are in the RESET state. A negative pulse applied to F.F.0 will switch it to the SET state. The counter now registers 00001.

A second negative pulse applied to F.F.0 will trigger it back to the RESET state. As this happens, though, a negative pulse is generated at the $\bar{1}$ output of F.F.0 which is applied to the COMPLEMENT input of F.F.1, triggering it to the SET state. Thus, the counter now registers 00010. The negative pulse at the $\bar{1}$ output was produced as Q1's collector voltage suddenly dropped from $+12$ volts to 0 volts when F.F.0 changed states. Similarly, F.F.2 changes state each time F.F.1 switches back to the RESET state; F.F.3 changes each time F.F.2 switches to RESET, and so on. Thus, F.F.0 changes state each time a pulse is applied to the counter input; F.F.1 changes every second time a pulse is applied; F.F.2, every fourth time; F.F.3 every eighth time; and F.F.4 every sixteenth time.

Binary counters can be built to count up to any number simply by adding more flip-flop stages. Any counter will count up to $(2^n - 1)$ counts, where n equals the number of flip-flop stages.

It is often desirable to count directly in the decimal system. A four-stage binary counter can be made to count to $(10)_{10}$ by adding a few AND gates. This counter normally has a capacity of 15 counts ($2^4 - 1 = 15$), but the gates reset the counter to 0 when a tenth pulse is received.

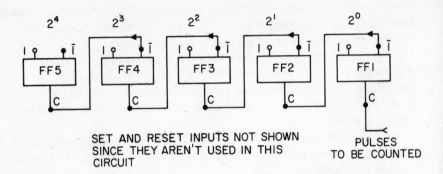

SET AND RESET INPUTS NOT SHOWN
SINCE THEY AREN'T USED IN THIS
CIRCUIT

PULSES
TO BE COUNTED

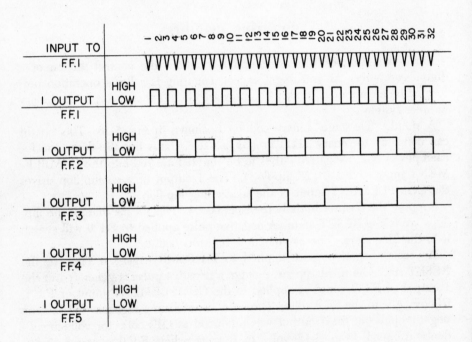

FIG. 5-16.   A five-stage binary counter.

DELAY CIRCUITS

Delay circuits are used to *delay* the travel of pulse signals for a short length of time. Most of these circuits have one input terminal and one output terminal. If a pulse is fed into the input, nothing happens immediately. After a short, fixed length of time, however, a similar pulse appears at the output.

A common delay circuit is the monostable multivibrator — a flip-flop circuit with only one stable state. An input pulse switches temporarily to an unstable state, from which it switches back after a short, constant length of time. When this happens, an output pulse is generated.

A typical monostable multi is shown in Fig. 5-17. It is similar to a flip-flop circuit, except that the collector of Q2 is coupled to the base of Q1 with a capacitor only. Since the capacitor blocks dc, Q1 can remain saturated only a short time after an input pulse cuts Q2 off.

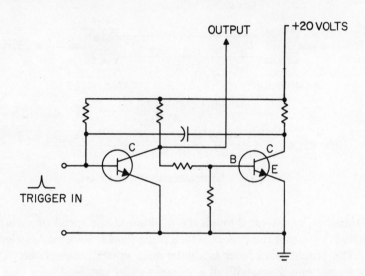

FIG. 5-17.   A transistor monostable multivibrator.

Some computers are equipped with non-electronic delay devices called *delay lines*. The simplest delay line consists of a long length of coaxial cable. A pulse applied to one end will not appear at the other end immediately. It takes a short time for the pulse to travel through the cable. Since electrical signals travel very quickly through cables, very long lengths are necessary for delays of even a few millionths of a second. As a result, electro-acoustic delay lines have been developed.

Electro-acoustic lines make use of the fact that the speed of sound in a metal or solid is much lower than the speed of an electrical signal on a wire.

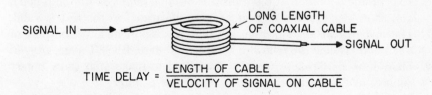

$$\text{TIME DELAY} = \frac{\text{LENGTH OF CABLE}}{\text{VELOCITY OF SIGNAL ON CABLE}}$$

FIG. 5-18.   A coaxial cable delay line.

These delay lines consist of three parts: an input transducer, a sound conducting medium and an output transducer. The input transducer is analagous to a loudspeaker, although it is usually made of quartz crystal. An electrical pulse is transformed into a sound pulse by the input transducer, and is fed into the sound conducting medium. Typical mediums include columns of mercury and specially-shaped quartz blocks.

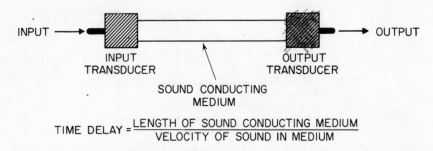

$$\text{TIME DELAY} = \frac{\text{LENGTH OF SOUND CONDUCTING MEDIUM}}{\text{VELOCITY OF SOUND IN MEDIUM}}$$

FIG. 5-19.   An electro-acoustic delay line.

The sound pulse travels through the medium at the speed of sound, and then strikes the output transducer, which transforms it back into an electrical signal. The output transducer is similar to a crystal microphone. Delays of close to one one-thousandth of a second can be obtained with long electro-acoustic delay lines.

REVIEW QUESTIONS

1. List and explain the major categories of electronic circuits used in digital computer calculating and control sections.
2. Describe the action of diodes, transistors, and vacuum triodes when used as two-state, switch-like devices.
3. Explain the operation of the "diode logic" AND gate; OR gate.
4. Explain how it is possible to compensate for unwanted logical inversions (complementing) of gate outputs.
5. Describe DCTL and RTL logic circuits. What are the advantages and disadvantages of each?
6. Explain the operation of the transistor bistable multivibrator (flip-flop), and show that the mechanical analogy illustrated in the text is valid.
7. List and explain the functions of the three inputs and two outputs of a flip-flop. Define the following terms: SET state; RESET state; trigger.
8. Show how six flip-flops may be connected to make a six-stage binary counter. What is the count capacity of this counter?
9. Explain the operation of the monostable multivibrator delay circuit.
10. List and explain the operation of the different types of delay lines.

6—Calculating Circuits

Now that we have discussed the basic digital computer building blocks, and have seen how Boolean algebra can be used "mathematically" to describe the logical design process, we are ready to investigate actual calculating circuitry.

The arithmetic section is the functional heart of a digital computer, since computer mathematics really consists of the four basic arithmetic operations, performed over and over again. Modern computer arithmetic sections are far more versatile and can perform other operations necessary for data processing and automatic control. Nevertheless, addition, subtraction, multiplication and division remain the most important operations.

REGISTERS

The four basic arithmetic operations are similar in that two numbers are manipulated to produce an answer. Both numbers must be present in the arithmetic section before an operation can be performed. This means that the arithmetic section must have a set of storage devices built into it that can temporarily hold both numbers while they are being manipulated. These storage devices are called *registers*.

A register is an assembly of bistable circuits capable of storing a certain amount of information in binary number form. The length of a register is the maximum amount of information it can store. Usually, the length of a register is one computer word. Thus, a register has the same capacity as a memory location. As described in Chapter 2, a particular word may be either a numerically coded instruction or a problem number. The arithmetic section is only concerned with problem numbers.

An arithmetic section will contain several registers. They will each have different names and perform different functions, but all of them operate along similar lines. A register that is capable of storing n binary digits is made of n bistable circuits, each one storing a single digit. Register operation will be described in terms of flip-flop bistable circuits. The reader should keep in mind, though, that other bistable circuits can and have been used to construct registers.

Three basic register operations are *clear-register, complement-register* and *transfer*. The names of these operations are sufficiently self-descriptive.

It is usually necessary to clear a register before new information can be transferred into it. A typical register will contain several flip-flops. Simultaneously applying a pulse to the RESET inputs of all the flip-flops destroys any information the register contains. All the flip-flops will switch to the RESET (or 0) state, and the register will then contain 0000000 . . . . This operation is known as clear-register.

Notice that an external pulse is required to clear a register. This pulse will normally be supplied by the control section when an instruction orders it to clear a specific register. For the present we will not be concerned with where or how this pulse and other *command pulses* are produced. We will observe, though, that the control section exercises its command over the arithmetic section by generating command pulses that are applied to certain circuits within the arithmetic section. The destination of these pulses and when they are generated depend on the information contained in the instruction words.

As defined in Chapter 3, the complement of a binary number may be formed by changing all of the 0's to 1's, and all of the 1's to 0's. We learned in the last chapter that a flip-flop has a built-in provision for complementing the binary digit it is storing. A pulse applied to the COMPLEMENT terminal will cause the circuit to either "flip" or "flop," whichever is appropriate, and change from one stable state to the other. Therefore, to complement a binary number stored in a flip-flop register, it is only necessary to apply a pulse simultaneously to all of the flip-flop COMPLEMENT inputs.

Since the complement of a binary number can be produced so quickly and easily, subtraction using the "complement addition process" is practical and efficient in computer calculations. This operation is called complement-register.

Nearly all computer operations involve a transfer of information from one register to another. Two often-used information transfer techniques are illustrated in Figs. 6-1 and 6-2. The first is called the *clear before transfer* operation. Each flip-flop in the "top" register is joined to its counterpart in the "bottom" register with an AND gate. Transferring a word from the "top" register to the "bottom" register is a two-step operation:

1. The "bottom" register is cleared by simultaneously pulsing its flip-flop's RESET inputs.
2. A *transfer* pulse is simultaneously applied to the AND gates.

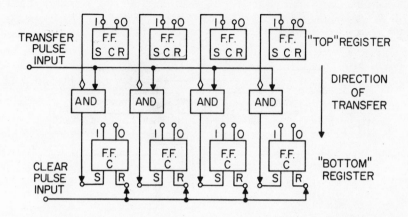

FIG. 6-1. A between-register transfer method: clear before transfer.

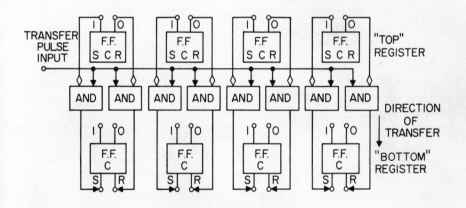

FIG. 6-2. A between-register transfer method: "jam" transfer.

The individual AND gates will SET the bottom register flip-flops they are connected to, only if the corresponding "top" register flip-flops are in the SET state.

A faster transfer technique is called the *jam transfer* operation, because the contents of the "top" register are literally "jammed" into the "bottom" register. No clear-register operation is required, thereby increasing the speed of transfer, but two AND gates are necessary for each corresponding pair of flip-flops. Simultaneously applying a transfer pulse to the AND gates transfers the "top" register's word to the "bottom" register, regardless of the previous contents of the "bottom" register.

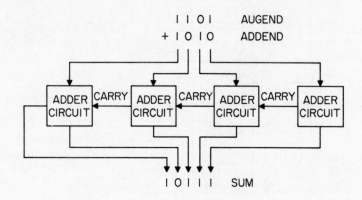

FIG. 6-3.   Binary numbers are manipulated by groups of simple circuits. Each circuit handles one pair of digits; the results are combined
to form the final answer.

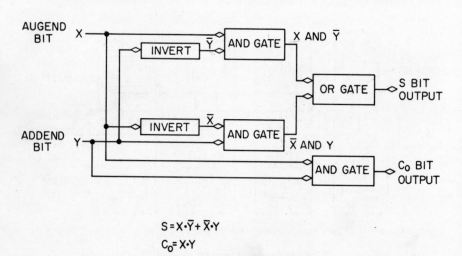

$$S = X \cdot \bar{Y} + \bar{X} \cdot Y$$
$$C_0 = X \cdot Y$$

X	Y	S BIT OUTPUT	C_0 BIT OUTPUT
0	0	0	0
1	0	1	0
0	1	1	0
1	1	0	1

FIG. 6-4.   A binary-digit half adder circuit.

ADDITION CIRCUITS

The five digital computer building block circuits handle electrical signals that represent single bits. We might expect, therefore, that the most basic calculating circuitry, built by combining various building blocks, manipulates pairs of single bits. This is actually the case; complete binary numbers are manipulated by groups of these basic calculating circuits.

A basic calculating circuit found throughout the arithmetic section is our old friend the binary digit adder. The correct name for this circuit is the *half adder*. You'll recall that the half adder adds two binary digits to produce a sum bit and a carry bit. We thoroughly investigated its properties and design in Chapter 4. These are reviewed in Fig. 6-4.

If the addend and the augend bits are stored in flip-flops, and the flip-flops are connected directly to the half adder, a simpler half adder circuit can be used. No inverters are required because the complement of each input bit is already available at the $\bar{I}$ outputs of the flip-flops. This simplified circuit is shown in Fig. 6-5.

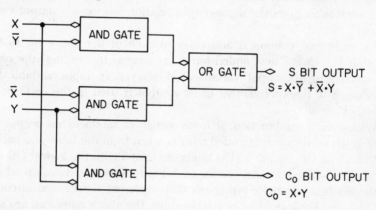

FIG. 6-5. A half adder circuit for use with flip-flops where $\bar{X}$ and $\bar{Y}$ signals are available.

The "half" in half adder is a reminder that this circuit does not perform the complete addition operation. A single half adder can be used to add two individual binary digits together, but a group of half adders cannot be used to add two binary numbers together. The reason for this is that the half adder is not equipped to handle *carry-in* digits. Consider the following binary addition example:

$$
\begin{array}{r}
101101 \quad \text{(augend)} \\
+ \ 110111 \quad \text{(addend)} \\
\hline
011010 \quad \text{(partial sum)} \\
1 \ \ 1 \ 1 \quad \text{(carry-overs)} \\
\hline
1100100
\end{array}
$$

Notice that carry-over digits are produced when the first, third and sixth columns of bit pairs are added together. These must be carried-in to the second, fourth and seventh columns, respectively.

The half adder circuit has no way of adding carry-in digits produced by the addition of preceding pairs of addend and augend digits.

The *full adder* circuit has a third input that accepts carry-in digits. Groups of full adders may be used to add binary numbers. Since the full adder circuit is a fundamental digital computer calculating circuit, we will derive its building block arrangement by starting with the logical design principles we've studied.

LOGICAL DESIGN OF A FULL ADDER CIRCUIT

You'll recall that the logical design of a digital computer circuit involves the following steps:

1. The desired properties of the circuit are clearly stated in a set of input-output relationship tables. One table is drawn for every output — that is, each table gives the input-output relationship for one output variable only.
2. An additional column is added on to each of the above tables to list "anded" terms. These anded terms are formed by "anding" the symbols representing the input variables. Whenever an input variable has a value of 0, the *complement* of its symbol is used in the corresponding anded term.
3. Whenever a combination of input variables produces an output equal to 1, the corresponding anded term is taken from the table and used as a term in an OR equation (the terms are joined with the logical OR operation). These equations, one for each input-output relationship table, are the Boolean algebraic equations that represent the desired circuit.
4. Using the Boolean identity relationships, the above equations are simplified; the number of logical operations in the equations are reduced, if possible.
5. The simplified equation is translated into the circuit it represents. Each logical connective operation (AND or OR symbol) it contains corresponds to one gate (AND gate, OR gate, respectively) in the circuit. Every complemented term (NOT symbol) corresponds to one inverter building block in the circuit. The required building blocks are arranged so that their individual inputs and outputs follow the form of the equation.

As we said earlier, a full adder has three inputs: an augend bit X, an addend bit Y and the possible carry-in bit C_i from the previous bit-pair addition. It has two outputs: a sum bit S, and a carry-over bit C_o that will be passed on to the next successive adder. The full adder actually finds the sum and carry-over bits for the addition of three binary digits. Therefore, our first step in specifying the desired properties of the circuit is to consider the "three binary digit addition table" shown in Fig. 6-6. This table is an extension of the two-digit table we studied earlier. Notice that there are *eight* possible combinations of three digits.

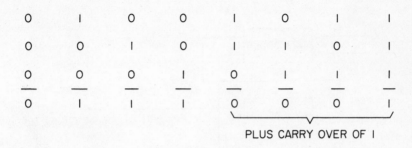

PLUS CARRY OVER OF I

FIG. 6-6.   The three binary digit addition table.

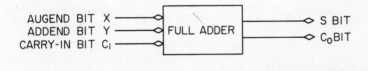

INPUTS			OUTPUT		INPUTS			OUTPUT	
X	Y	C_i	S BIT	"ANDED" TERMS	X	Y	C_i	C_o BIT	"ANDED" TERMS
O	O	O	O	$\bar{X}\cdot\bar{Y}\cdot\bar{C_i}$	O	O	O	O	$\bar{X}\cdot\bar{Y}\cdot\bar{C_i}$
I	O	O	I	$X\cdot\bar{Y}\cdot\bar{C_i}$	I	O	O	O	$X\cdot\bar{Y}\cdot\bar{C_i}$
O	I	O	I	$\bar{X}\cdot Y\cdot\bar{C_i}$	O	I	O	O	$\bar{X}\cdot Y\cdot\bar{C_i}$
I	I	O	O	$X\cdot Y\cdot\bar{C_i}$	I	I	O	I	$X\cdot Y\cdot\bar{C_i}$
O	O	I	I	$\bar{X}\cdot\bar{Y}\cdot C_i$	O	O	I	O	$\bar{X}\cdot\bar{Y}\cdot C_i$
I	O	I	O	$X\cdot\bar{Y}\cdot C_i$	I	O	I	I	$X\cdot\bar{Y}\cdot C_i$
O	I	I	O	$\bar{X}\cdot Y\cdot C_i$	O	I	I	I	$\bar{X}\cdot Y\cdot C_i$
I	I	I	I	$X\cdot Y\cdot C_i$	I	I	I	I	$X\cdot Y\cdot C_i$

FIG. 6-7.   Input-output relationship tables for the full adder.

The two full adder input-output relationship tables (one for the S bit output, and one for the C_o bit output) follow directly from the above three-digit addition table, and are shown in Fig. 6-7. Notice that the "anded" terms have been included. Removing from both tables the "anded" terms that correspond to output bits equal to 1, and joining them together with the logical OR function, we obtain two Boolean algebraic equations that represent the full adder's building block arrangement:

For $S = 1; \bar{S} = 0$
$$S = \bar{C}_i \cdot \bar{X} \cdot Y + \bar{C}_i \cdot X \cdot \bar{Y} + C_i \cdot \bar{X} \cdot \bar{Y} + C_i \cdot X \cdot Y$$

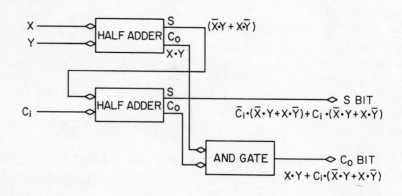

FIG. 6-8.   A full adder circuit.

$S = \bar{C}_i \cdot (\bar{X} \cdot Y + X \cdot \bar{Y}) + C_i \cdot (\bar{X} \cdot \bar{Y} + X \cdot Y)$
$C_o = X \cdot Y + C_i \cdot (\bar{X} \cdot Y + X \cdot \bar{Y})$

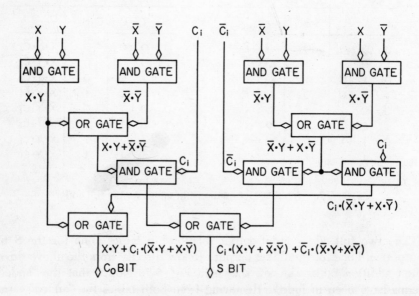

FIG. 6-9.   Another full adder circuit.

For $C_o = 1$; $\overline{C}_o = 0$
$$C_o = \overline{C}_i \cdot X \cdot Y + C_i \cdot X \cdot \overline{Y} + C_i \cdot \overline{X} \cdot Y + C_i \cdot X \cdot Y$$

The first equation describes four possible input combinations that produce an S output bit equal to 1; the second equation gives the four input combinations that result in the C_o output bit equaling 1. It is left as an exercise for the reader to show, with the help of truth tables, that these equations are valid.

There are several possible ways to simplify these equations, so several different building block arrangements can be derived. Two correct full adder circuits are shown in Figs. 6-8 and 6-9. The simplified equations corresponding to these circuits appear below. (The numbers indicated next to the steps in the simplification correspond to the numbers on the list of Boolean algebraic identities and relationships given in Chapter 4.)

For $S = 1$
$$S = X \cdot \overline{Y} \cdot \overline{C}_i + \overline{X} \cdot Y \cdot \overline{C}_i + \overline{X} \cdot \overline{Y} \cdot C_i + X \cdot Y \cdot C_i$$
$$S = \overline{C}_i \cdot (\overline{X} \cdot Y + X \cdot \overline{Y}) + C_i \cdot (\overline{X} \cdot \overline{Y} + X \cdot Y) -$$
$$\text{Relationship } \#10$$

but
$$C_i \cdot (\overline{X} \cdot \overline{Y} + X \cdot Y) = C_i \cdot (\overline{\overline{X} \cdot \overline{Y}}) \cdot (\overline{X \cdot Y}) -$$
$$\text{Relationship } \#19$$

and
$$C_i \cdot (\overline{\overline{X} \cdot \overline{Y}}) \cdot (\overline{X \cdot Y}) = C_i \cdot (X \cdot Y) \cdot (\overline{X} \cdot \overline{Y})$$
$$= C_i \cdot (X \cdot Y \cdot \overline{X} \cdot \overline{Y}) = C_i \cdot (X \cdot \overline{Y} \cdot \overline{X} \cdot Y)$$
$$= C_i \cdot (X \cdot \overline{Y}) \cdot (\overline{X} \cdot Y) = C_i \cdot (\overline{X} \cdot Y + \overline{Y} \cdot X) -$$
$$\text{Relationship } \#19$$

Therefore,
$$S = \overline{C}_i \cdot (\overline{X} \cdot Y + X \cdot \overline{Y}) + C_i \cdot (\overline{\overline{X} \cdot Y + X \cdot \overline{Y}})$$

For $C_o = 1$
$$C_o = \overline{C}_i \cdot X \cdot Y + C_i \cdot \overline{X} \cdot Y + C_i \cdot X \cdot \overline{Y} + C_i \cdot X \cdot Y$$
$$C_o = X \cdot Y \cdot (C_i + \overline{C}_i) + C_i \cdot (\overline{X} \cdot Y + \overline{X} \cdot Y) - \text{Relationship } \#10$$
$$C_o = X \cdot Y + C_i \cdot (\overline{X} \cdot Y + X \cdot \overline{Y}) - \text{Relationship } \#6$$

For $S = 1$
$$S = \overline{C}_i \cdot (\overline{X} \cdot Y + X \cdot \overline{Y}) + C_i \cdot (\overline{\overline{X} \cdot Y + X \cdot \overline{Y}})$$

For $C_o = 1$
$$C_o = X \cdot Y + C_i \cdot (\overline{X} \cdot Y + X \cdot \overline{Y})$$

To illustrate the use of the full adder circuit, we can combine three of them to make a *parallel* adder capable of adding two three-digit binary numbers. The word "parallel" means that the three pairs of corresponding digits in the numbers are added simultaneously. A *serial* adder, on the

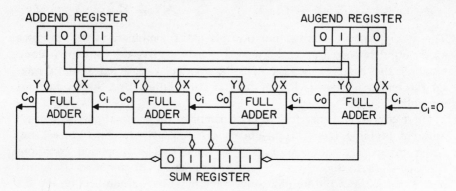

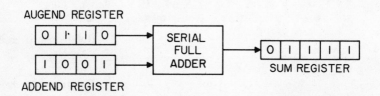

FIG. 6-10.   Parallel and serial addition methods.

other hand, will add the digit pairs sequentially; the 2^0 column would be summed first, followed by the 2^1 column. The difference between serial and parallel methods of addition is illustrated in Fig. 6-10.

A THREE-DIGIT PARALLEL ADDER

Since the three digit pairs will be summed simultaneously by the parallel adder, three individual full adder circuits are necessary, one for each digit pair.

The addend and augend numbers Y and X, respectively, will be temporarily held in two three-flip-flop registers. Therefore, the second full adder circuit described above can be used, since the complement of each augend and addend bit is available at the $\overline{1}$ outputs of the corresponding flip-flops.

The sum of the two binary numbers will be stored in a third flip-flop register. This register must have four flip-flops, since the sum of two three-digit binary numbers is a four-digit binary number. For example:

$$
\begin{array}{r}
101 \\
+\ 100 \\
\hline
1001
\end{array}
$$

The complete parallel adder circuit is pictured in Fig. 6-11. Operation of the circuit is as follows. First, the sum register is cleared by a clear-register operation. Then, an add command pulse is applied simultaneously to the *add line* AND gates. If the S output bit of a full adder is equal to 1, then a 1 is stored in the corresponding flip-flop of the sum register. The fourth flip-flop (2^3) of the sum register is set by the carry-over bit from the third full adder stage. This happens because each AND gate will produce a pulse output when the add command pulse is applied only if the S bit fed into it equals 1. Also, the outputs of the AND gates are connected to the SET inputs of the sum register flip-flops. Thus, each flip-flop will receive a SET input pulse from its AND gate only when the corresponding S bit output equals 1.

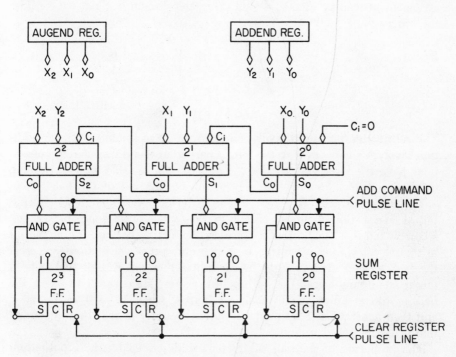

FIG. 6-11.   A three-stage parallel adder.

SUBTRACTION

In Chapter 4 we discussed two methods for subtracting one binary number from another: 1) direct subtraction, according to the rules of the binary subtraction table; and 2) adding the "complement" of the subtrahend to the minuend, and then adding the final carry to the first column of the sum.

Most digital computers use the second method, since it eliminates the need for special subtracting circuitry; the adder circuits can do double duty. As we discovered earlier, it is very easy to complement any binary number stored in a flip-flop register. The only additional equipment required is a few control circuits and a circuit that will add the end-around carry to the first digits of the sum of the minuend and complement of the subtrahend.

Before we discuss the complement method in detail, let's consider the direct subtraction method. This technique is occasionally applied, and the development of the required circuitry will provide us with another illustration of logical design procedures.

The same logical design methods used to derive the adder building block arrangements can be used to design subtracter circuitry. First, we consider the binary digit subtraction table:

$$
\begin{array}{cccc}
0 & 1 & 1 & 0 \\
-\,0 & -\,0 & -\,1 & -\,1 \\
\hline
0 & 1 & 0 & 1
\end{array}
$$

with a borrow of 1

The subtraction operation involves a "borrow" from the left, whereas addition involves a carry-over to the left. Apart from this difference, the operations have the same general form. From the above table we can develop the binary *half subtracter*, the subtraction counterpart of the half adder.

The half subtracter is a four terminal device: two inputs — a minuend bit, M, and a subtrahend bit, N; and two outputs — a difference bit, D, and a borrow bit, B. The borrow is considered an output because it is an output in digital calculating circuitry. In pencil and paper calculations, we treat the borrow as a digit brought into a subtraction, not a digit sent out. It might seem paradoxical, but both points of view are correct. In effect, the half subtracter automatically makes a borrow when $M = 0$ and $N = 1$, and then generates a 1 bit at the B output in order to tell the next circuit that it has borrowed from it.

The properties of the half subtracter are described by the input-output relationship tables in Fig. 6-12. Note that the "anded" terms have been included.

We can quickly write the Boolean algebraic equations that represent the correct building block arrangement by considering the tables in Fig. 6-12.

$$\text{For } D = 1, \bar{D} = 0$$
$$D = M \cdot \bar{N} + \bar{M} \cdot N$$

$$\text{For } B = 1, \bar{B} = 0$$
$$B = \bar{M} \cdot N$$

FIG. 6-12.   Input-output relationship tables for the half subtracter.

INPUTS		OUTPUT	"ANDED" TERMS
M	N	D	
0	0	0	$\overline{M} \cdot \overline{N}$
I	0	I	$M \cdot \overline{N}$
0	I	I	$\overline{M} \cdot N$
I	I	0	$M \cdot N$

INPUTS		OUTPUT	"ANDED" TERMS
M	N	B	
0	0	0	$\overline{M} \cdot \overline{N}$
I	0	0	$M \cdot \overline{N}$
0	I	I	$\overline{M} \cdot N$
I	I	0	$M \cdot N$

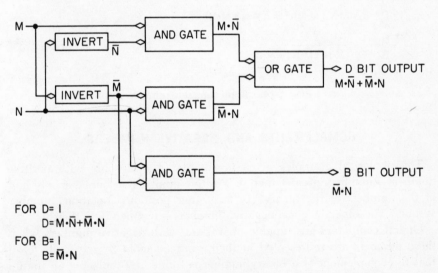

FOR D= I
$\quad$ D= M·$\overline{N}$+$\overline{M}$·N
FOR B= I
$\quad$ B=$\overline{M}$·N

FIG. 6-13.   A half subtracter circuit.

Notice that the difference-term equation is identical to the sum-term equation of the half adder. This simplifies the task of translating the logical symbols into a building block arrangement. The complete half subtracter is shown in Fig. 6-13.

Just as the half adder could not be used as the adding device in a multi-digit binary number addition circuit, the half subtracter is not suitable for use in binary number subtraction circuits. The half subtracter has no "borrow-out" input that "tells" it that the previous subtracter has borrowed from it. The *full subtracter* illustrated in Fig. 6-14 must be used. It is left as an exercise for the reader to show that the input-output relationship tables, Boolean equations, and building block arrangement are valid.

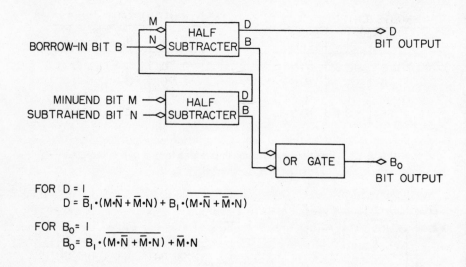

FOR D = I
$$D = \bar{B}_I \cdot (M \cdot \bar{N} + \bar{M} \cdot N) + B_I \cdot \overline{(M \cdot \bar{N} + \bar{M} \cdot N)}$$

FOR B_O = I
$$B_O = B_I \cdot \overline{(M \cdot \bar{N} + \bar{M} \cdot N)} + \bar{M} \cdot N$$

FIG. 6-14.   A full subtracter circuit.

COMPLEMENTS AND NEGATIVE NUMBERS

The numerical examples given in Chapter 4 dealt only with positive numbers — numbers greater than 0. Positive numbers account for only half of the numbers in the binary (or any other positional notation) number system. The other half are negative numbers — numbers less than 0.

Digital computers are capable of working with negative numbers when these numbers are represented in their *complemented* form. You'll recall that the complement of a binary number is formed by replacing all the 0's with 1's, and all the 1's with 0's. Subtraction may be performed by adding the complement of the subtrahend to the minuend, as reviewed in the following example:

Direct Subtraction		Complement Method	
10110	(minuend)	10110	(minuend)
− 10010	(subtrahend)	+ 01101	(complement of 10010)
00100	(difference)	⌐1 00011	(sum of minuend and complement of 10010)
		└→ + 1	(end-around carry)
		00100	(difference)

Notice that the final carry-over from the sum of the minuend and complement of the subtrahend is added to the first digit of the sum. This is often called the *end-around carry* operation. The above example illustrated a subtraction. However, a little thought will show that this subtraction is equivalent to an addition in which $+10110$ is the augend and -10010 is the addend:

$$
\begin{array}{ll}
10110 & \text{(minuend)} \\
-\ 10010 & \text{(subtrahend)} \\
\hline
+\ 00100 & \text{(difference)}
\end{array}
\qquad
\begin{array}{c}
\text{equivalent} \\
\text{to}
\end{array}
\qquad
\begin{array}{ll}
10110 & \text{(augend)} \\
+\ (-10010) & \text{(addend)} \\
\hline
+\ 00100 & \text{(sum)}
\end{array}
$$

It is evident that the complement of a binary number actually represents the negative of that number. Thus, a computer will handle negative numbers by working with their complements. For example, -110111 will be handled as 001000; -101010 will be handled as 010101.

We have used "$+$" and "$-$" signs to indicate positive and negative numbers. Such signs are meaningless to a computer, which recognizes only electrical signals representing 0 and 1. This problem is solved by adding an additional bit ahead of every binary number to indicate the sign. This bit is called, naturally enough, the *sign bit*. A sign bit equal to 0 indicates a positive number; a sign bit equal to 1 indicates a negative number. An asterisk (*) is used to set the sign bit off from the number bits when the number is recorded on paper. No such symbol is needed inside the computer.

$$
\begin{array}{rcl}
0*1000110 & = & +\ 1000110 \\
1*0111001 & = & -\ 1000110 \\
0*1000001 & = & +\ 1000001 \\
1*0111110 & = & -\ 1000001 \\
0*0000001 & = & +\ 0000001 \\
1*1111110 & = & -\ 0000001
\end{array}
$$

The examples above illustrate number words that are eight bits long: one sign bit plus seven number bits. Notice that a 1 sign bit tells us that the number bits represent the complement of a number that has a minus sign ($-$) in front of it.

In add and subtract calculations, the sign bit is treated as one of the digits of the number. The carry-over digit produced when the sign bits of two numbers are added to the end-around carry that is added to the first digit of the sum. The following examples will illustrate the procedures of binary addition and subtraction using binary numbers having sign bits:

Problem Stated "on Paper"	Calculation Performed in Computer	
1001101 + 0011010 = ?	0*1001101	(augend)
	+ 0*0011010	(addend)
	0*1100111	(sum)
1111111 + (−1000000) = ?	0*1111111	(augend)
	+ 1*0111111	(addend in complement form)
	1 0*0111110	
	+ 1	(end-around carry)
	0*0111111	(sum)
1000000 − 0111111 = ?	0*1000000	(minuend)
	+ 1*1000000	(complement of subtrahend)
	1 0*0000000	
	+ 1	(end-around carry)
	0*0000001	(difference)

THE ACCUMULATOR

Accumulation is simply a process of repeated addition, as performed by an *accumulator* within the arithmetic section of a digital computer. As its name suggests, an accumulator keeps a running total of preceding additions, and supplies its contents as the augend for every succeeding addition. Roughly speaking, an accumulator is the "kissing cousin" of the parallel adder. There are, however, a few basic differences. Since an accumulator of one type or another is the heart of most arithmetic sections, we will investigate this device in detail.

You'll recall that a parallel adder accepts two binary numbers as inputs, and generates their sum as an output. Three separate registers are required: one for the augend, one for the addend, and a third for their sum. An accumulator, on the other hand, accepts only one binary number at a time. As each number is received, it is added to the number already contained within the accumulator, forming a new sum. The two key points to remember about accumulators are: 1) only one number at a time is accumulated; and 2) the number stored within an accumulator at any given time is the sum of all the numbers that have been fed into it up to that time.

If you check back to Chapter 2, you'll understand that when we said "the contents of the arithmetic section" in describing the various instructions, we actually meant "the contents of the accumulator." In fact, the list of instructions states the operations that an accumulator, along with various control circuits, can perform.

An accumulator requires only two registers: one to hold the new addend number (new number being accumulated), and one to store the running total of preceding additions. This running total is called the *accumulated total*, and it is stored in the accumulator register, or A register, for short. The register holding the addend number is sometimes called the X register.

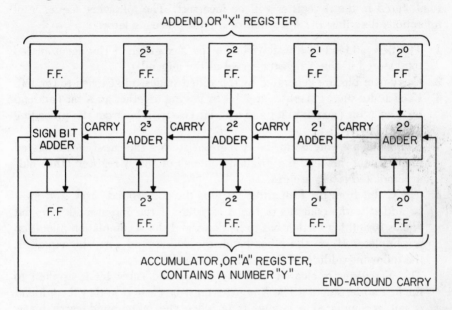

FIG. 6-15.   A five-stage accumulator.

Figure 6-15 is a rough block diagram depicting the major elements of a five-stage accumulator. The fifth adder is called the *sign bit* adder. It handles the sign bits as described in the last section. Thus, the largest accumulated total that can be accommodated before the accumulator "overflows" is $(1111)_2$ or $(15)_{10}$. Notice the double arrows between the A register flip-flops and the five adder circuits. These indicate that there is a double flow of binary digits between the flip-flops and adder circuits. First the A register supplies the augend (the "old" accumulated total) for an addition. Then it receives the "new" accumulated total. This dual flow of bits makes it necessary for the accumulator to operate in a sequential fashion; each accumulation consists of a sequence of discrete steps, or "suboperations."

Sequential operation is necessary so that the correct carry-over digits are generated by each adder stage. You'll recall that the value of the carry-over bit of an adder depends on the value of the addend and augend bits applied as inputs. In an accumulator, the augend bits to be applied to the adders are stored in flip-flops in the A register. But, these same flip-flops will contain the sum of the addend and augend bits at the end of the addition process. Obviously, the augend bit and the sum bit may have different values. Therefore, all of the adder stages must generate their carry-over bits *before* the sum bits are generated and entered into the A register.

A little thought will show that if this is not done, the new accumulated total stored in the A register will be incorrect. The following sequence of operations describes the operation of a typical accumulator:

1. The new addend is transferred into the X register. (The accumulated total stored in the A register serves as the augend.)
2. Carry-over bits are generated by the added stages, and carried to the left.
3. Each adder stage generates an S bit by adding together an X bit (addend bit), an A bit (augend bit) and a C_i bit (carry-in bit from the preceding adder stage).
4. The S bits are entered in the A register, storing the "new" accumulated total. In the process, the original contents of the A register (the "old" accumulated total) are lost.
5. The C_o bit from the fifth adder stage is the end-around carry, and must be added to the contents of the A register. If the end-around carry bit equals 0, nothing further has to be done, and the accumulation operation is complete. If, on the other hand, the end-around carry bit equals 1, the following additional steps are performed:
6. The X register is cleared, and the end-around carry bit is applied to the first adder stage. (The X register must be cleared so that the addend is not accumulated a second time when the end-around carry bit is added.)
7. Steps 2, 3 and 4 are performed over again. The net effect is to add the end-around carry bit to the "new" accumulated total.

The individual adder circuits of an accumulator are very similar to the full adder circuits described earlier. Since the addend and augend bits are stored in flip-flops, the complements of these inputs are available. Some additional building blocks must be added to effect the transfer of the S bit into the A register flip-flops. Figure 6-16 is the diagram of an accumulator adder stage that uses no inverter building blocks. This means that the complements of all terms must be available in the circuit. The additional equations that represent the circuits that deal with the complement terms are derived from the same input-output tables as are those for the non-complemented term circuitry. These equations are written by combining the "anded" terms that were left over when the original equations were derived. (These "anded" terms correspond to combinations of the input variables that produce a 0 output.)

The two AND gates and one OR gate enclosed by dotted lines in Fig. 6-16 make up a circuit that transfers the S bit output of the adder to the A

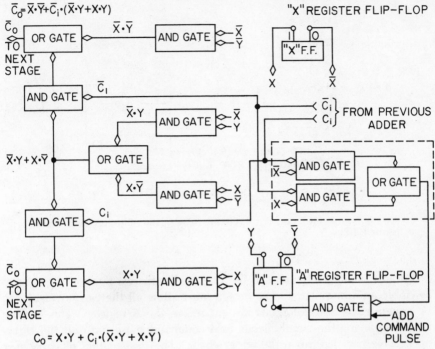

FIG. 6-16.   The accumulator adder stage.

register flip-flop. Actually, this circuit decides whether or not to COMPLE-MENT the flip-flop. Since the A register already contains a binary digit at the start of the addition (the augend bit), there is a possibility that this bit is the same value as the S bit.

For example, suppose that the inputs to the adder are: X bit = 0; A bit = 1; and C_i bit = 0 ($\bar{C}_i$ bit = 1). In this case, the outputs will be: S bit = 1; and C_o bit = 0 ($\bar{C}_o$ bit = 1). The S bit output must be placed in the A register flip-flop. However, this flip-flop already contains 1 (is in the SET state) since the augend bit equals 1. Nothing has to be done to the flip-flop.

The simple three-gate circuit, often called a *bit comparator*, compares the S bit output with the bit stored in the A register flip-flop. If the S bit is the same as the A bit, the flip-flop is left undisturbed. If, on the other hand, the S bit is not of the same value as the A bit (S ≠ A), the comparator COMPLEMENTS the A register flip-flop when the Add command pulse is received.

The Boolean equation representing the comparator circuit can be derived from the adder input-output relationship table by grouping the "anded" terms that correspond to S bit not equal to A bit. The circuit follows directly from the simplified equation (Fig. 6-17).

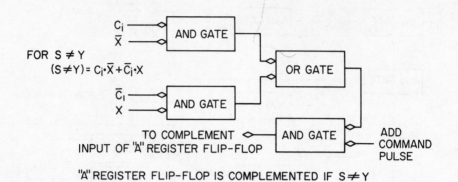

FIG. 6-17. A bit comparator circuit. A register flip-flop is complemented if $S \neq Y$.

A chain of adder circuits can be combined with two flip-flop registers to assemble an accumulator. The design must allow all the carry-over bits to be generated before the S bits are entered in the A register. This is done by *not* applying the simultaneous Add command pulse until all the carry-overs have traveled down the adder chain. The propagation of carry-over bits down the adder chain is started by applying a pulse to the NOT carry-in input, $\overline{C}_i$, of the first adder stage. This is the same as saying that the carry-in bit, C_i, to the first stage equals 0, since if $\overline{C}_i$ equals 1, then C_i equals 0. When the flow of carry-over bits is complete, the Add command pulse can be simultaneously applied to the adder stages, transferring the S bits into the A register.

The complete diagram for the five stage accumulator we discussed earlier is shown in Fig. 6-18. The *complement pulse line* allows the contents of the X register to be complemented. Thus, to perform subtraction, the minuend is placed in the A register, and the subtrahend in the X register. Sometime before the Add command pulse is applied, the X register is complemented, forming the complement of the subtrahend. After the end-around carry operation is completed, the A register will contain the difference of the minuend and subtrahend.

The end-around carry circuitry adds the carry-over generated by the fifth adder stage to the sum of the addend and the augend. If the C_o bit produced by the fifth adder equals 1, the *end-carry gate* will generate a pulse that does three things when the Add command pulse is applied. First, the pulse clears the flip-flops of the X register, setting the register to zero. Second, the pulse is applied to the C_i input (carry-in bit input) of the first adder stage. Finally, the pulse becomes a new Add command pulse after being delayed for a short period of time. The short delay is necessary to allow the carry-over pulse applied to the first adder stage to travel down the adder chain.

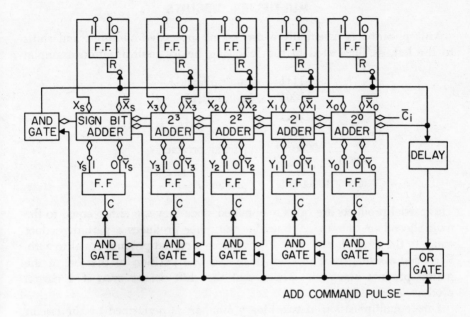

FIG. 6-18.   A five-step accumulator circuit.

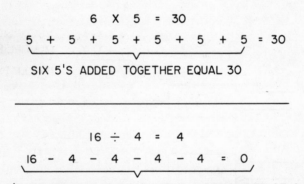

$$6 \times 5 = 30$$

$$5 + 5 + 5 + 5 + 5 + 5 = 30$$

SIX 5'S ADDED TOGETHER EQUAL 30

$$16 \div 4 = 4$$

$$16 - 4 - 4 - 4 - 4 = 0$$

FOUR 4'S SUBTRACTED FROM 16 LEAVE A REMAINDER OF 0

Fig. 6-19.   Multiplication is repeated addition. Division is repeated subtraction.

Since the X register contains zero, and a 1 has been carried into the first adder stage, the net effect is to add 1 to the contents of the A register.

The accumulator can perform multiplication and division by repeated addition or repeated subtraction, respectively. Fig. 6-19 illustrates how multiplication and division can be accomplished in this manner.

MULTIPLIER CIRCUITS

Multiplication is essentially a process of successive additions and shifts to the left, as illustrated in the following binary multiplication example:

$$
\begin{array}{ll}
1111 & \text{(multiplicand)} \\
1001 & \text{(multiplier)} \\
\hline
1111 & \\
0000 & \\
0000 & \text{(partial products)} \\
1111 & \\
\hline
10000111 & \text{(product)}
\end{array}
$$

The partial products are quickly obtained since they are either equal to the multiplicand or to zero. A 1 in the multiplier produces a partial product equal to the multiplicand, and a 0 produces a partial product equal to zero. Each successive partial product is shifted one position to the left of the partial product above it. Notice that the shift occurs even if a partial product is equal to zero.

Direct multiplication of two binary numbers is performed by the circuit illustrated in Fig. 6-20. The "shifts" are performed by physically placing

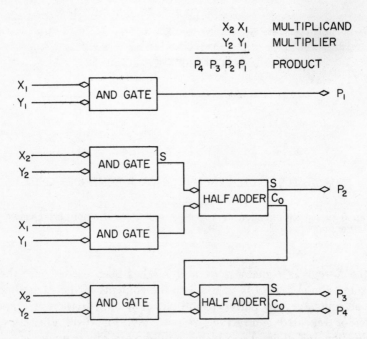

FIG. 6-20.   Direct multiplication of two two-digit numbers.

logical building blocks in the correct positions. The circuit shown can multiply two four-digit binary numbers. Notice that the *product register* has a capacity of four bits, since the product of two two-bit binary numbers is a four-digit binary number.

REVIEW QUESTIONS

1. Explain the function and design of a flip-flop register.
2. Describe the basic register operations. Explain the difference between the "clear-before-transfer" and "jam transfer" methods.
3. Show how a group of circuits, each capable of handling a single pair of bits, can manipulate complete binary numbers.
4. Explain why the binary digit adder (half adder) cannot be used in an adding circuit that will sum two binary numbers.
5. Explain the major difference between the two full adder circuits diagramed in this chapter.
6. Explain the operation of an accumulator by contrasting it to a "parallel adder."
7. Describe the operation of the "end-around carry" circuitry of the accumulator. Why is the fifth adder stage called the "sign bit adder"?
8. Verify that the full subtracter circuit diagramed in the text has the required input-output relationship.
9. Explain how negative numbers are represented in digital computers.
10. Verify that the direct multiplication circuit diagramed in the text can actually perform multiplication.

7—Control Circuits

The preceding chapters have described the theory and operation of electronic circuits that can perform arithmetic. Calculating circuitry alone, however, does not make up a digital computer. Automatic operation, necessary for high-speed computation, requires control circuitry that can interpret the program of instructions and command the operation of the arithmetic circuits accordingly.

We said earlier that control circuitry is spread throughout a digital computer, and that the term "control section" is just a convenient label that groups these circuits together. This doesn't mean, though, that control in a computer is loose or haphazard. Quite the contrary is true.

In many respects, a computer is similar to an army. The commanding general exercises control over every man, but he doesn't give each man his orders directly. Rather, he commands subordinate officers, who in turn command their subordinates, and so on down the line, until the lowest ranking recruit has been told what to do. This process is called the "chain of command."

A similar chain of command exists within a digital computer. The "general" is the programmer, and his "orders" are the program of instructions. After the instructions have been fed into the computer, the commands they contain are "passed down through the ranks" by the various control circuits, until they reach the "troops"—the thousands of logical building blocks.

In this chapter we will study the "top" of the chain of command: the circuitry that interprets the program instructions and generates appropriate command signals which are sent to the "lower ranking" control circuitry throughout the computer.

The reader should understand that these circuits will be discussed in very general terms, and that the examples given apply only to the very simple digital computer described in this chapter. It will be apparent, however, that these basic principles may be extended to the largest automatic digital computers.

THE MACHINE CYCLE

We discussed programming techniques for a *stored program* digital computer in Chapter 2. A program of numerically coded instructions is stored within the memory section along with corresponding problem numbers. These instructions are examined one at a time by an interpreting device that then generates electrical signals that cause the called-for operation to be performed. Many different methods for doing this have been developed, as witnessed by the many different kinds of digital computers that have been designed.

One of the simplest approaches is to have the machine operate on a cyclical basis. The computer *periodically* takes a new instruction out of memory, examines it, decodes it, performs the specified operation, and then goes back to memory for another instruction. This sequence of steps may be called a *machine cycle*.

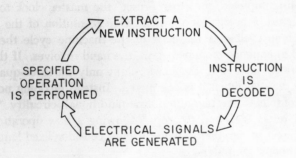

FIG. 7-1.   The machine cycle.

In many digital computers, every machine cycle is the same length. That is, it always takes the same amount of time to complete the above series of steps, regardless of the operation called for. A single machine cycle must be long enough to allow:

1. An instruction to be extracted from the memory section.
2. The instruction to be fed to the interpreting device and decoded.
3. The command signals to be sent to the appropriate circuitry.
4. The specified operation to be performed.

Digital computers that operate in this manner are called *synchronous computers*. *Asynchronous* computers are similar, except that the machine cycles are not all the same length. Obviously, some arithmetic operations require more time to perform than others. In a synchronous computer, the machine cycle must be set to accommodate the slowest operation. Thus, time is wasted when fast operations are performed.

In asynchronous machines, on the other hand, a different length machine cycle is available for each operation. The computer looks for the next instruction immediately after the operation is completed, instead of waiting for the beginning of a fixed-length machine cycle.

Asynchronous machines are faster than synchronous computers, but are also more complicated. The computer described in this chapter is a synchronous machine. Strictly speaking, the term synchronous refers to any computer whose operation is *synchronized* by *timing pulses* produced by some kind of "master clock." As we shall soon see, these timing pulses coordinate the electrical signals that control the calculating circuits, and guarantee that each step of an operation is performed at the proper time in the sequence.

Considering the above definitions of synchronous and asynchronous computers, it may seem paradoxical to add that it is possible to build a synchronous computer that has a variable length machine cycle. The basic control circuits of such a computer are almost the same as described above, with one exception: there are additional circuits that sense when an operation has been completed, and then "reset" the master clock to "zero." To illustrate, picture a pocket stop watch. One revolution of the hand represents a machine cycle. At the start of the machine cycle the hand is at "zero." As the sequence of steps begins, the hand revolves. If the operation being performed is simple, the hand might only be three-quarters of the way around the dial when it is completed. Instead of doing nothing while the hand completes its revolution, the additional circuitry "pushes the button" and resets the hand to "zero," allowing a new operation to begin.

In the interest of simplicity, we will only consider fixed-length machine cycle synchronous computers.

BASIC

The best way to illustrate the logical design of control circuitry is to actually develop the control circuits for a simple computer. Our first step is to name the computer — every self-respecting computer has to have a name! Let's call it BASIC, which stands for Basic Automatic Stored Instruction Computer.

Now, we must decide what operations BASIC will be able to perform. Since BASIC is just an illustrative computer, we will set the word length to twelve binary digits, and give BASIC 256 memory locations with addresses ranging from 00000000 to 11111111.

We listed the fundamental computer instructions in Chapter 2, and saw how they may be used to solve complicated mathematical problems. By considering multiplication to be repeated addition, and division to be repeated subtraction (as outlined in the last chapter) we can simplify the list of instructions. The following table indicates the instructions that BASIC will respond to. Notice that a new set of operation code numbers, written in binary notation, is used.

COMMAND	SYMBOL	OPERATION CODE	MEANING (A sequence of steps)
Clear and Add	CAD	0001	1. Clear accumulator register. 2. Transfer number stored at specified operation data address to X register. 3. Add the contents of X register to accumulator.
Add	ADD	0010	1. Transfer number stored at specified operation data address to the X register. 2. Add the contents of the X register to accumulator.
Store	STR	0011	1. Transfer the contents of the accumulator to memory buffer register. 2. Transfer contents of memory buffer register to the specified operation data address.
Subtract	SUB	0100	1. Transfer number stored at specified operation data address to the X register. 2. Complement the X register. 3. Add the contents of the X register to accumulator. 4. Handle the end-around carry.
Jump	JUP	0101	1. Transfer the number stored at specified operation data address to program counter.
Jump if minus	JIM	0110	1. Examine the sign bit of accumulator. 2. If sign bit is 1, transfer number stored at specified operation data address to program counter.
Print	PRT	0111	1. Transfer contents of accumulator to output section. 2. Start output mechanism.
Start	START	1000	Start Computer.
Stop	STOP	1001	Stop Computer.

The "meaning" column in the above table shows that the instructions themselves involve a sequence of steps that the computer must perform in the given order. The timing of these steps is very important. As we observed in the last chapter, error-free operation of an accumulator depends on the arrival of command pulses at the proper time. In other words, BASIC's control circuitry must be able to generate and send command pulses to the proper calculating circuits at the correct time if the above instructions are to be carried out.

BASIC's control circuitry must include the following equipment:

1. Instruction interpreter: a device that will decode the operation code number of each instruction and determine which of the nine operations has been called for.
2. Memory control circuits: circuitry that can transfer the contents of any specified memory location to the arithmetic or control sections and store a word in any specified memory location.
3. Program counter: a counting circuit that keeps track of the memory address of the "next" instruction to be performed.
4. Master timing device: an internal "clock" which will make sure that the individual steps in an instruction are performed at the correct time.
5. Command pulse generator: a device that applies command pulses to the calculating circuits. Signals from the instruction interpreter tell the generator where to apply command pulses; signals from the master timing device tell it when to apply the pulses.

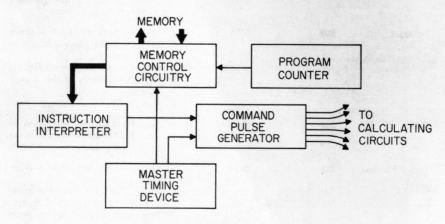

FIG. 7-2.   BASIC's control circuitry.

DECODING INSTRUCTIONS

Every instruction is composed of two parts: an operation code number, and an operation data address. You'll recall that the operation code number specifies the operation to be performed, while the operation data address gives the memory location involved in the operation. BASIC is capable of nine different operations, hence there are nine different operation code numbers: 0001 through 1001. One of these code numbers forms the first four digits of every instruction word. Interpreting an instruction, therefore, consists of *decoding* the operation code number that the instruction contains.

At the start of each new machine cycle an instruction word is withdrawn from the memory section, and its first four bits (the operation code number) are fed to the *operation decoding matrix*. The operation decoding matrix has nine output terminals, one corresponding to each of BASIC's operations. The voltage level at a given output terminal will be "high" only if the corresponding instruction code number has been fed into the decoding matrix. For example, the voltage level of the "clear and add" output terminal will be "high" if the code number 0001 has been fed into the decoding matrix.

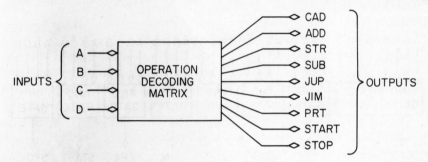

FIG. 7-3.   The operation decoding matrix.

It is readily apparent that the operation decoding matrix must have four inputs, one corresponding to each of the digits of the operation code number. For convenience we will call the four inputs A, B, C and D. The table lists the input-output relationships for the operation decoding matrix:

INPUT-OUTPUT RELATIONSHIP TABLE
FOR OPERATION DECODING MATRIX

Inputs				Outputs								
A	B	C	D	CAD	ADD	STR	SUB	JUP	JIM	PRT	START	STOP
0	0	0	1	1	0	0	0	0	0	0	0	0
0	0	1	0	0	1	0	0	0	0	0	0	0
0	0	1	1	0	0	1	0	0	0	0	0	0
0	1	0	0	0	0	0	1	0	0	0	0	0
0	1	0	1	0	0	0	0	1	0	0	0	0
0	1	1	0	0	0	0	0	0	1	0	0	0
0	1	1	1	0	0	0	0	0	0	1	0	0
1	0	0	0	0	0	0	0	0	0	0	1	0
1	0	0	1	0	0	0	0	0	0	0	0	1

Design Equations

$$CAD = \bar{A} \cdot \bar{B} \cdot \bar{C} \cdot D$$
$$ADD = \bar{A} \cdot \bar{B} \cdot C \cdot \bar{D}$$
$$STR = \bar{A} \cdot \bar{B} \cdot C \cdot D$$
$$SUB = \bar{A} \cdot B \cdot \bar{C} \cdot \bar{D}$$
$$JUP = \bar{A} \cdot B \cdot \bar{C} \cdot D$$

$$JIM = \bar{A} \cdot B \cdot C \cdot \bar{D}$$
$$PRT = \bar{A} \cdot B \cdot C \cdot D$$
$$STOP = A \cdot \bar{B} \cdot \bar{C} \cdot \bar{D}$$
$$START = A \cdot \bar{B} \cdot \bar{C} \cdot D$$

After being withdrawn from memory, each instruction word is placed in an *instruction register*, where it is temporarily held until it has been carried out. The first four flip-flops of this twelve flip-flop register contain the operation code number. The 1 outputs of these flip-flops are connected to the appropriate inputs of the decoding matrix. Thus, when an instruction is transferred from memory to the instruction register, one of the nine outputs of the decoding matrix automatically generates a "high" voltage level that represents the called-for operation. As indicated by the Boolean design equations in the above table, the decoding matrix circuit is quite simple and straightforward. It consists of nine, four-input AND gates, as shown in Fig. 7-4.

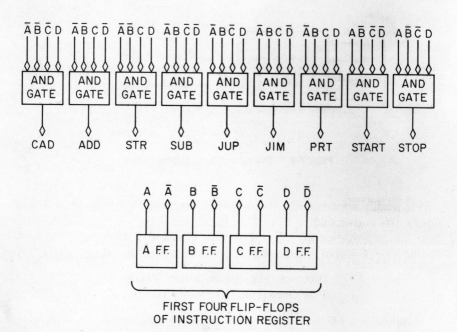

FIG. 7-4.   The operation decoding matrix circuit.

MEMORY CONTROL CIRCUITS

Both numerically coded instructions and problem number words are fed into the memory section by the programmer at the start of a computer calculation. Memory control circuits that can transfer the contents of any memory location to the correct register in the arithmetic or control section are necessary. An instruction word, for example, must be moved to the instruction register at the start of every machine cycle, while problem numbers must be sent to the various registers in the accumulator during every calculation. In addition, the same memory control circuits must be able to place words into any specified memory location. This is required to carry out the STR (Store) instruction.

The individual memory locations are actually one-word registers. The next chapter describes the bistable devices used in memory registers (ferrite cores). Removing a word from memory entails transferring a "replica" of the stored word; the contents of the register are left undisturbed. Thus, the same word can be taken out of memory any number of times. Putting a word into memory, on the other hand, destroys the original contents of the location in which it is stored.

BASIC's memory section consists of three units which we will treat as "black boxes": the memory locations (256 individual registers), the memory control circuitry, and an additional external register called the buffer register.

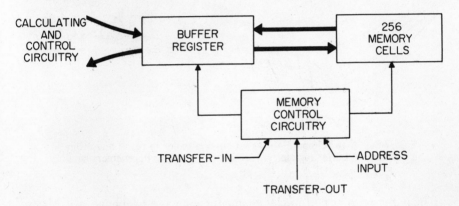

Fig. 7-5.   BASIC's memory section.

The memory control circuit "block box" has three inputs: the "transfer into memory command pulse" input; the "transfer out of memory command pulse" input; and the "address of memory location involved in transfer" input. The first two will be called the "Transfer-in" and "Transfer-out" inputs, respectively, and the third will be called the "Address" input.

Feeding the address of a desired word into the Address input and then applying a command pulse to the Transfer-out terminal will cause the word to be transferred to the buffer register.

Feeding a selected address into the Address input and then pulsing the Transfer-in command input will cause the word contained in the buffer register to be stored at the specified address.

The memory control circuitry mainly performs transfer operations, and consists of circuits similar to those we discussed in the last chapter in the section on transferring numbers between registers.

The *buffer register* is necessary to "isolate" the memory registers from the rest of the computer. High-speed operation requires that the memory be of the "random access" variety, and that parallel wire transfer techniques be employed. This means that a wire must run between each flip-flop in the buffer register and the corresponding bistable elements of every memory register — digit to digit, in other words. Without a buffer register it would be necessary to run "random access lines" from every memory location to every register in the calculating and control circuits.

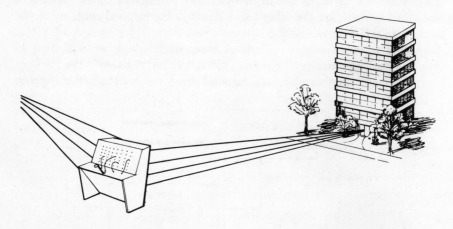

FIG. 7-6.   A switchboard allows an outside caller to reach any office in a building. A buffer register is the "switchboard" for the memory section.

The buffer register performs the same function as a telephone switchboard in a large office building. The offices (which are analagous to the memory registers) are connected to the switchboard. A phone call from the outside doesn't go directly to an office, it first goes through the switchboard. Thus, a caller can contact any or all of the offices without having a separate telephone line to each office. One line to the switchboard is all that's necessary.

PROGRAM COUNTER

A vital control operation is that of keeping track of the sequence of instructions. Obviously, the computer must carry out instructions in the exact order set down by the programmer. BASIC will remove instructions from memory in numerical order. If the first instruction is at location 00000000, the second instruction will be at location 00000001, the third at 00000010, and so on. Keeping track of the instruction memory locations is a counting operation performed by the *program counter*, a binary counting circuit.

At the start of a program "run," the address of the first instruction is entered into the program counter. When this instruction is transferred to the instruction register, a pulse is applied to the "count input," raising the count of the program counter by 1. The content of the program counter is now the address of the second instruction.

For example, suppose the address of the first instruction is 00000000. As this instruction is transferred out of memory, a pulse is applied to the program counter, raising its count by 1. The program counter will now contain 00000001, the address of the second instruction. When the second instruction is removed from memory, the program counter is pulsed again, raising its count to 00000010, the address of the third instruction, and so on. Thus, the number contained in the program counter is always the address of the next instruction to be performed.

This process of transferring instructions from memory, followed by stepping up the count of the program counter by 1, continues until the program is completed, or until a "jump" instruction is reached. In the event that the jump conditions exist, the control circuitry will clear the program counter, and then enter the jump instruction's operation data address. Thus, the memory control circuits will extract the next instruction from the location called for by the jump instruction.

TIME PULSE DISTRIBUTOR: A MASTER TIMING DEVICE

Picture a clock face having a single hand rotating at high speed. This clock represents BASIC's machine cycle. At the start of the cycle, the hand points straight up. As the hand begins its trip around the dial, the memory control circuits go into action, first transferring an instruction word out of memory into the instruction register, and then transferring the problem word located at the instruction's operation data address into the buffer register.

Somewhere past "four o'clock" the operation code number is interpreted by the decoding matrix, and the calculating circuits go into operation. The problem number is shifted from the buffer register to the accumulator, and manipulated according to the commands of the instruction. This process takes between "two and eight hours," depending upon the arithmetic operation performed. It's now almost "twelve o'clock," and BASIC is getting ready for the next machine cycle.

Notice the importance of timing when the various operations are performed during the machine cycle. Figure 7-7 illustrates the complete machine cycle for the SUB (subtract) operation, and gives the "hour" at which each step of the operation takes place. The first five "hours" of the cycle are used to extract a new instruction from memory, interpret it, and transfer the problem number word from the specified operation data address to the buffer register. Since a new instruction must be obtained at the start

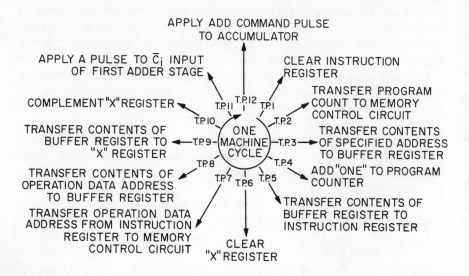

FIG. 7-7.   The machine cycle for the SUB operation.

of each cycle, it is clear that the first five "hours" of any machine cycle will follow the above sequence.

BASIC actually contains a "clock" that controls the timing of every machine cycle. It isn't a mechanical clock with a rotating hand, but rather a *time pulse distributor*. BASIC's time pulse distributor is nothing more than a pulse generator with twelve separate output terminals. Each output produces a pulse during the machine cycle corresponding to one of the twelve "hours" in the above model.

What we've done is split the machine cycle into twelve equal time periods. The twelve time pulses generated by the time pulse distributor indicate when each period begins. More important, they are the actual command pulses that activate the various memory control and calculating circuits.

The first five timing pulses, T.P. 1 through T.P. 5, are applied to the memory control circuit to extract a new instruction and transfer it to the operation data register. After the first five steps are complete, and the instruction has been decoded, T.P. 6 through T. P. 12 will be routed through the calculating circuits and applied as command pulses. The routing job is performed by a network of gates controlled by the instruction decoding matrix. (The next section discusses this gate network.)

An important point to note is that the lengths of the twelve time intervals are sufficient to allow any single calculation or memory control operation to be performed. Thus, for example, in any interval a word might be transferred from memory to the buffer register, or a sum might be formed in the accumulator.

BASIC may be started or stopped simply by turning on or turning off the time pulse distributor. The start-stop circuitry is designed so that a START instruction begins the machine cycle with T.P. 1, and a STOP instruction stops the computer after T.P. 12 has been generated.

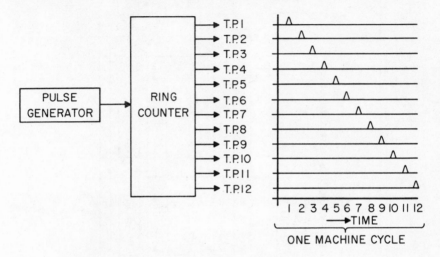

FIG. 7-8.   The time pulse distributor.

The time pulse distributor is basically a modified binary counter, often called a "ring counter." Twelve flip-flops and associated gates are connected in a ring, as illustrated in Fig. 7-9A & B. This circuit counts the output of a precise pulse generator. The generator pulse rate is adjusted so that twelve pulses are generated in the time allotted to one machine cycle. In operation, the first flip-flop in the ring, F.F.1, is set to the SET (or 1) state by a start pulse. The SET condition is stepped around the ring, advancing one flip-flop each time a pulse is produced by the pulse generator. Notice that only one out of the twelve flip-flops are in the SET state at any time. In effect, the circuit separates the twelve pulses produced by the pulse generator during each cycle into twelve separate pulses, each appearing at a different output at a different time during the cycle. Applying a STOP pulse "opens" the ring, interrupting the cycle after T.P. 12 has been generated.

COMMAND GENERATOR

The function of routing timing pulses throughout BASIC's calculating circuitry and applying them to the appropriate command pulse inputs is

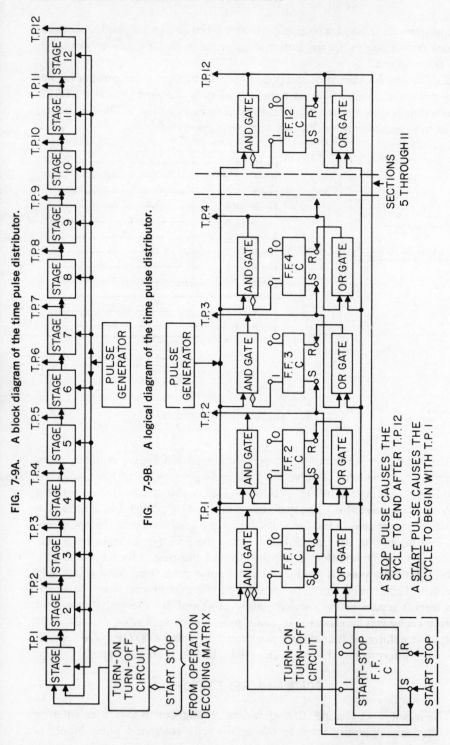

FIG. 7-9A.   A block diagram of the time pulse distributor.

FIG. 7-9B.   A logical diagram of time pulse distributor.

A STOP PULSE CAUSES THE CYCLE TO END AFTER T.P.12

A START PULSE CAUSES THE CYCLE TO BEGIN WITH T.P.1

performed by networks of AND gates, often called *command generators*. Seven individual command generators are required, one for each of BASIC's operations with the exception of START and STOP. As we mentioned earlier, BASIC is started by turning on the time pulse distributor and stopped by turning it off. Command pulses for these two operations are produced directly by the instruction decoding matrix.

Each of these seven operations consists of several individual steps. As we said earlier, these "sub-operations" must be performed at the proper time during the machine cycle.

The first five time pulses are used to extract an instruction from memory and place it in the instruction register where it is interpreted. Since all machine cycles must start with a search for an instruction, the first five time pulses will always perform the following operations:

TIME PULSE	ACTION
T.P. 1	Applied to CLEAR input of instruction register to clear this register.
T.P. 2	Causes number registered in the program counter to be transferred to the Address input of the memory control circuitry.
T.P. 3	Applied to Transfer-out input of memory control circuitry. Instruction contained in specified location (specified by step 2) is transferred out of memory into the buffer register.
T.P. 4	Applied to the "count" input of the program counter, raising its count by 1. The program counter now contains the memory address of the next instruction to be performed.
T.P. 5	Causes the contents of the buffer register to be transferred to the instruction register. The instruction is automatically interpreted as the first four flip-flops of the instruction register are connected to the decoding matrix. The corresponding output terminal of the decoding matrix will be "high."

The remaining seven time pulses can be used to activate the appropriate circuitry to carry out the individual steps of the called-for operation. The table on pages 120 and 121 lists BASIC's operations (except START and STOP) in a broken-down form. The individual sub-operations are shown next to the time pulses that cause them to be performed.

As an illustration, let's consider the Subtract (SUB) instruction. This operation consists of seven separate sub-operations:

1. Clear the X register of the accumulator.
2. Transfer the specified operation data address to the Address input of the memory control circuitry.

Timing Pulse	CAD 0001	ADD 0010	STR 0011
T.P. 1 - T.P. 5	Extract instruction.	Extract instruction.	Extract instruction.
T.P. 6	Clear X and A registers.	Clear X register only.	Transfer operation data address to memory control circuits.
T.P. 7	Transfer operation data address to memory control circuits.	Transfer operation data address to memory control circuits.	Transfer contents of A register to buffer register.
T.P. 8	Transfer contents of specified address to buffer register. (Transfer-out)	Transfer contents of specified address to buffer register. (Transfer-out)	Transfer contents of buffer register to specified memory location. (Transfer-in)
T.P. 9	Transfer contents of buffer register to X register.	Transfer contents of buffer register to X register.	Not used.
T.P. 10	Pulse $\bar{C}_i$ input of first adder stage. (Carry-in 0 to 2° adder.)	Pulse $\bar{C}_i$ input of first adder stage. (Carry-in 0 to 2° adder.)	Not used.
T.P. 11	Apply Add command pulse.	Apply Add command pulse.	Not used.
T.P. 12	Not used.	Not used.	Not used.

TIMING PULSE	SUB 0100	JUP 0101	JIM 0110	PRT 0111
T.P. 1 - T.P. 5	Extract instruction.	Extract instruction.	Extract instruction.	Extract instruction.
T.P. 6	Clear X register only.	Clear program counter.	Examine sign bit. If 0, do nothing; if 1, proceed as follows:	Transfer contents of A register to output section.
T.P. 7	Transfer operation data address to memory control circuits.	Transfer operation data address to memory control circuits.	Clear program counter.	Not used.
T.P. 8	Transfer contents of specified address to buffer register. (Transfer-out)	Transfer contents of specified address to buffer register. (Transfer-out)	Transfer operation data address to memory control circuits.	Not used.
T.P. 9	Transfer contents of buffer register to X register.	Transfer contents of buffer register to program counter.	Transfer contents of specified address to buffer register. (Transfer-out)	Not used.
T.P. 10	Apply complement pulse to X register. (Complement-register)	Not used.	Transfer contents of buffer register to program counter.	Not used.
T.P. 11	Pulse $\bar{C}_i$ input of first adder stage. (Carry-in- 0 to 2° adder.)	Not used.	Not used.	Not used.
T.P. 12	Apply Add command pulse.	Not used.	Not used.	Not used.

3. Apply a pulse to the Transfer-out input of the memory control circuitry in order to transfer the contents of the specified operation data address to the buffer register. (We will assume that the buffer register uses "jam transfer" circuitry. Therefore, no clear-register operation is necessary.)

4. Transfer the contents of the buffer register to the X register.

5. Apply a pulse to the COMPLEMENT inputs of the X register's flip-flops in order to form the complement of the subtrahend. (The number stored at the specified operation data address of a SUB instruction is the subtrahend.)

6. Apply a pulse to the C_i (NOT carry-in) input of the first adder circuit in the accumulator, in order to propagate carry-overs throughout the accumulator.

7. Apply an Add command pulse to the accumulator. The accumulator will automatically handle the end-around carry, as described in the last chapter.

It is evident that the subtract operation command generator must route T.P. 6 to the clear command input of the X register; T.P. 7 to the transfer

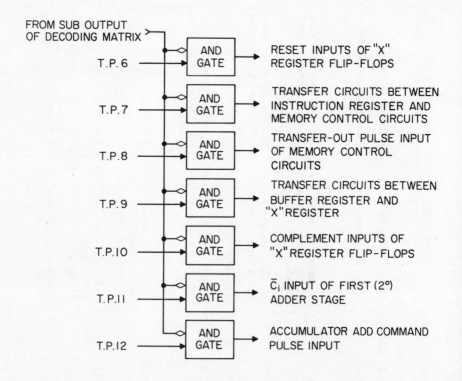

FIG. 7-10.   The SUB command generator.

circuits between the instruction register and the memory control circuitry; T.P. 8 to the Transfer-out input of the memory control circuitry; T.P. 9 to the transfer circuits between the buffer register and the X register; T.P. 10 to the COMPLEMENT inputs of the X register's flip-flops; T.P. 11 to the $\overline{C}_i$ input of the first adder stage; and T.P. 12 to the Add command pulse input of the accumulator.

The subtract operation command generator consists of seven two-input AND gates connected as shown in Fig. 7-10. One AND gate is used to produce each of the seven command pulses that must be "generated." Operation of the circuit is very straightforward. Timing pulses T.P. 6 through T.P. 12 are applied as inputs to the gates. The second input to each gate is the "SUB" output of the instruction decoding matrix. The outputs of the seven AND gates are connected to the appropriate calculating and memory control circuitry.

Thus, when the decoding matrix produces a SUB output, indicating that the present instruction calls for a subtraction, the subtraction command

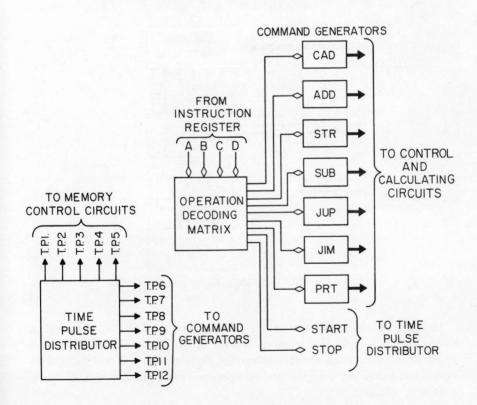

FIG. 7-11.   The command generating system.

generator sends command pulses to the proper circuits at the correct time, in order to carry out the command.

Operation of the six other command generators is similar, although the number and destination of command pulses will be different for each operation. Of course, each of the other command generators is activated by the corresponding output of the instruction decoding matrix. Fig. 7-11 illustrates the complete command generating system, and shows the command pulse outputs of the remaining six command generators.

The preceding discussion treated the various control circuits as individual devices. We know, though, that they must work together in perfect unison when BASIC is carrying out a program of instructions. The block diagram shown in Fig. 7-12 illustrates how the circuits are interconnected. Don't be misled by the apparent complexity of the arrangement. The circuit is actually quite simple, and easy to follow.

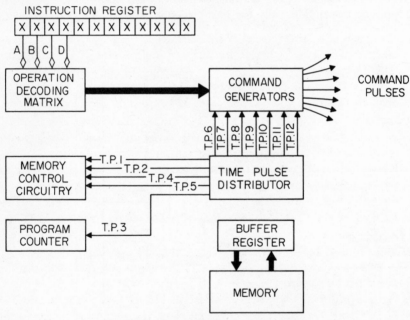

Fig. 7-12.   BASIC's control system.

Here's a quick description of the circuits in Fig. 7-12. At the start of every machine cycle the *memory control circuits* transfer an instruction from the memory section to the instruction register. Once there, the instruction is treated as two components: an operation code number and an operation data address.

The first five pulses produced by the *time-pulse distributor* accomplish the above operations.

The *program counter* keeps track of the address of the next instruction. Its contents increase by 1 when T.P. 4 is applied to its "count" input terminal. At the beginning of the next machine cycle, the memory control circuitry extracts a new instruction from the address registered in the program counter.

Since the first four flip-flops of the instruction register (those that contain the operation code number) are connected to the inputs of the *operation decoding matrix*, one of the output terminals of the decoding matrix will be "high." This terminal corresponds to the called-for operation. This output signal activates the corresponding *command generator*, which then routes timing pulses T.P. 6 through T.P. 12 to the appropriate command pulse inputs of the calculating and memory control circuitry.

REVIEW QUESTIONS

1. Explain the function and design of the "program counter."
2. Show why the "buffer register" is necessary.
3. Describe the three inputs to the "memory control circuitry," and discuss their functions.
4. Explain the meaning of "machine cycle."
5. Explain the difference between synchronous and "asynchronous" computers.
6. Describe the circuitry of the "operation decoding matrix." Show how it is connected to the "instruction program."
7. Explain the function of the "time pulse distributor," and show, by tracing the path of a pulse, that only one flip-flop of the "ring counter" is in the SET state at any time.
8. Explain why no "command generators" are required for the START and STOP operations.
9. Explain, in a step by step fashion, how the first five time pulses are used to extract a new instruction from the memory section at the start of every machine cycle.
10. Write a program that will command BASIC to add the four numbers A, B, C and D. Remember that you must place these numbers in the memory section first.

8—Memory Devices

One reason digital computers have acquired the nickname "electronic brain" is that they can store information. Memory has always been closely linked with the human thinking process, so it doesn't seem too far-fetched to believe that if a machine can remember it can also think. Of course, a computer doesn't think for itself, it merely follows the programmer's instructions to the letter. However, a computer's ability to operate automatically at high speed goes hand in hand with its ability to store instructions and problem data, and "remember" them at the proper time. This chapter will be a brief survey of the most widely used memory devices.

As we mentioned in Chapter 2, a digital computer memory section may include several kinds of storage devices. No single "ideal" memory system has been developed that can efficiently perform all of the storage functions required by a large computer. Before discussing the different memory devices, let's run through a few of the terms used to describe them all:

Capacity. The capacity of a storage device refers to the maximum number of bits (or, sometimes, words) that can be stored within it. Complex calculations, involving many instruction and data words, require a large memory capacity.

Access time. Access time refers to the length of time it takes the memory control circuits to transfer the contents of any specified address out of the memory section; or the length of time required to store a word at a given address.

Kind of access. Memory devices can be categorized into two groups: random access memories and sequential access memories. In random access systems the control circuitry can go directly to any specific location. In sequential access memories, the control circuitry must pass by other locations to reach the specified one. A magnetic tape memory is a sequential access device since locating a specific word recorded on the tape requires running past other words on the tape.

The access time of a random access memory is much lower than that of a sequential access memory, but sequential units usually have a much larger capacity and are simpler and less expensive than random access devices.

Permanence. The permanence or non-permanence rating of a memory system specifies whether or not the contents may be erased. All memories using magnetic devices are non-permanent since they can be erased.

Volatility. A memory device is *volatile* if the information stored within it is lost when the power is turned off.

Physical characteristics. Among the important physical characteristics of a memory device are size, power requirements, ruggedness, flexibility and cost. Cost is usually specified as the "cost per bit" or "cost per word." An expensive memory with a large capacity might have a lower cost per bit than a less expensive, small capacity unit.

The table on page 128 lists the commonly used memory devices along with a typical characteristic and their major application in computing systems.

Most large scale digital computers will have two memories: an internal memory and an external memory. The internal memory is used during computer operation and performs the memory functions we have discussed in previous chapters. The external memory serves as a kind of "reference library" for the computer, storing large quantities of data that are only occasionally called for.

Internal memories don't need a very large capacity, but must have a very short access time, and are usually of the random access variety. External memories can have a longer access time since they are not in constant use, and as they require an enormous capacity, sequential storage devices are suitable. A small "buffer memory," sometimes considered as a third memory, connects the internal and external memories. It performs much the same functions as the buffer register described in the last chapter.

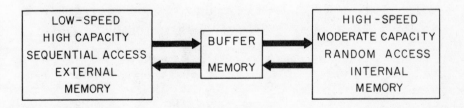

FIG. 8-1.   The buffer memory.

COMPARISON OF MEMORY DEVICES

DEVICE	KIND OF ACCESS	TYPICAL ACCESS TIME	CAPACITY	PERFORMANCE	USE
Punched Cards	Sequential	100 microseconds	80-90 characters/card	Non-erasable	High-capacity, low-speed external memory
Punched Tape	Sequential	Long	—	Non-erasable	High-capacity, low-speed external memory
Magnetic Drum	Sequential	50 microseconds	Over 2,000,000 bits/drum	Erasable	High-capacity, moderate speed internal memory.
Magnetic Tape	Sequential	Up to 75-100 seconds	Up to 25,000,000 bits/reel	Erasable	High-capacity, low-speed external memory
Magnetic Core	Random	1 to 25 microseconds	1 bit/core (matrices of 100,000 cores have been built)	Erasable	Moderate-capacity, high-speed internal memory

PUNCHED CARDS AND PAPER TAPE

Punched cards and punched paper tape are usually classified as input-output equipment rather than as memory devices, and probably see more service in these applications. However, they are very useful as low-cost high capacity external memories when their slow handling speed can be tolerated. Information is stored on punched cards and tape by means of a coded pattern of punched holes (see below). They are permanent memory devices, and once punched can be filed away until the information recorded is called for.

As every person living in the United States must know by this time, punched cards can be used to remember everything from the size of a pay check to the stock number of "an attractive little number" down at the local dress shop. Paper tape is not as familiar to the public, although it is used for much the same purposes.

Many coding techniques for punched cards and tapes have been suggested or are in actual use. The two most widely used punched card systems are those used by I.B.M. (International Business Machines, Inc.) and Remington Rand. They are similar to one another.

The I.B.M. card is divided into 80 vertical columns running the full width of the card. Each column has 12 punching positions. Therefore, a total of 960 bits can be stored on each card. A punched hole signifies a 1, an unpunched position a 0.

The Remington Rand card has 90 columns, with 12 punching positions per column, giving it a capacity of 1080 bits.

Paper tapes are either perforated according to a "5 channel" code or an "8 channel" code. These codes represent alphabetical and decimal digit characters rather than binary digits. Each character of the stored data is recorded in a single column.

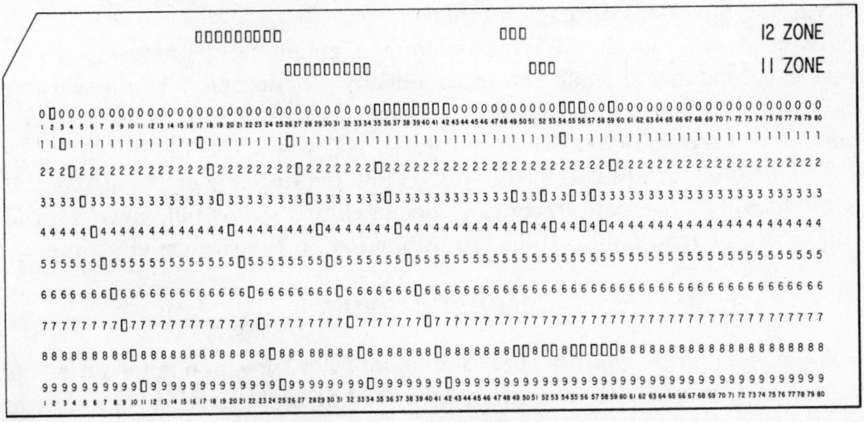

FIG. 8-2.   A typical punched card.

Punched cards and perforated tapes are "read" by a variety of devices. The most widely used devices employ wire brushes to "feel" the holes, or photoelectric cells to scan the hole pattern. Modern punched card readers can decode more than 2400 cards per minute.

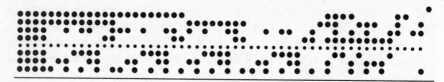

FIG. 8-3.   A typical perforated paper tape.

MAGNETIC RECORDINGS

Two important memory devices, the rotating magnetic drum and magnetic tape, store information by means of magnetic recordings. The major elements of any magnetic recording system are a *magnetic head,* energized by means of a coil fed by a signal current, and a suitable *magnetic recording* surface. The recording surface is a thin base of non-magnetic material that has been coated with a thin layer of ferromagnetic material, usually iron oxide.

In operation, the recording surface is moved past the head. A current of one polarity fed through the coil on the head will magnetize the surface just beneath the head in one direction. A current of reverse polarity will magnetize the surface in the other direction. A varying current will produce varying directions of magnetization as the surface is drawn past the head. Information in binary form is easily stored on a magnetic surface. Current of one polarity represents 1, and current of the other polarity represents 0. The surface will "remember" the information by storing it as a pattern of varying directions of magnetization.

To read out the stored information, the magnetized surface is drawn past a second head, built almost identically as the first. As the varying patterns of surface magnetization are drawn past the "read" head, a correspondingly varying signal is induced in the coil wound on the head.

The strip of surface that passes just below the heads is called a *track*. It is obvious that magnetic recording memories are sequential, since a head can record or read only one bit of information on the surface at a time.

MAGNETIC DRUM

A *magnetic drum* consists of an aluminum cylinder whose outer surface is coated with iron oxide. The drum is rotated at high speed, by an electric motor, past an array of magnetic heads. A single drum may contain hundreds of parallel tracks, each one a ring around the circumference. Bit

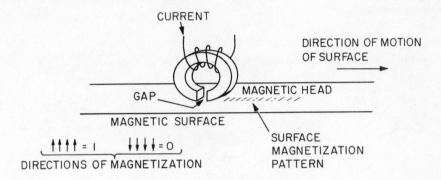

FIG. 8-4.   Magnetic recording.

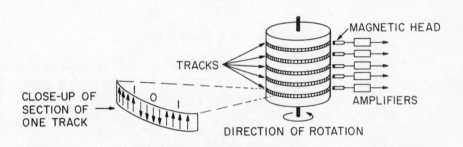

FIG. 8-5.   Rotating drum memory.

densities range from 50 to 300 bits per inch, and total storage capacities of over 2 million bits per drum are not unusual.

A drum memory requires synchronizing circuitry that can pinpoint any specific word written on the drum. Three different access times must be considered: minimum, maximum and average. Since the drum is rotating it may take some time before the desired word passes below the "read" head. This time delay is the access time.

If, by a stroke of good luck, the specified location spins by under the head just after it was called for, the time delay is very small. This is the *minimum access time*. If, on the other hand, the desired word went by the head just before it was called for, the drum must make one complete revolution before the word will pass the heads again. Thus, *maximum access time* is the time of one drum revolution.

Most of the time, though, the desired words will be in various positions with respect to the head, and we can define *average access time* as the average of the minimum and maximum access times. On the average, therefore, we may expect an access time equaling one-half the time of one drum revolution.

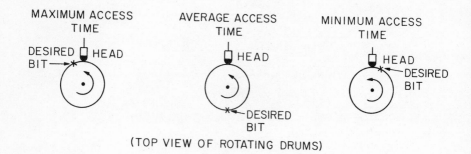

(TOP VIEW OF ROTATING DRUMS)

Fig. 8-6.   Drum access times.

MAGNETIC TAPE MEMORIES

The maximum capacity of any magnetic recording system depends on the total recording surface available. The geometry of a drum permits many tracks, but each track is relatively short, equaling the circumference of the drum. Magnetic tape recording systems use only one track, but that track may be several thousand feet long, and record millions of bits.

Tape memory systems are similar to home tape recorders in basic operation. Unlike home recorders, though, tape memory units operate at very high speed and are capable of almost instantaneous stops, starts and changes of direction, since words located anywhere along the tape may be called for.

You'll recall that the motion of the varying directions of surface magnetization past the "read" head induces the output in the coil. The tape must be going at a minimum speed for the output signal level to be sufficiently high. We might expect, therefore, that there will be a short time lag before a stopped tape is accelerated up to operating speed. To compensate for this, data are recorded on the tape in *data blocks* of several words, separated by small blank segments. The tape is always stopped with the "read" head positioned above the center of one of these segments. When the tape is moved, it will reach operating speed before the edge of the nearest data block passes beneath the "read" head.

The main drawback of tape memories is their long access time. Reading-out a specified word can involve winding through a whole reel of tape, if the word is on the end of the tape and the head is above the beginning. For this reason, tape memories are used to store bulk data and reference information.

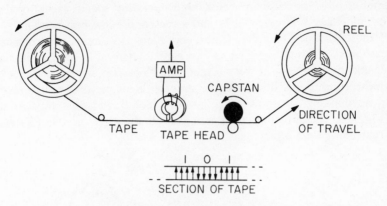

FIG. 8-7.   A simplified diagram of a magnetic tape recorder.

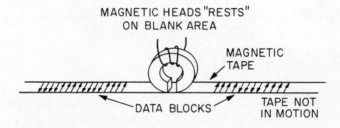

FIG. 8-8.   Data blocks on a magnetic tape.

FERRITE CORE MEMORY SYSTEMS

The internal memories of nearly all electronic computers consist of a large number of one-word registers built of bistable elements. Early machines used relay or vacuum tube flip-flops, but the large physical size and power requirements of these circuits set a practical upper limit on the memory's capacity. As has been noted before, many other bistable elements have been developed. One of these, the ferrite core, has become the most widely used memory device in modern computers.

Ferrite cores used in computer memory systems are made by shaping a finely powered mixture of oxides, metallic salts and organic binder into a *toroid*, or doughnut shape, and then sintering it at high temperatures. The tiny core of magnetic ceramic material that is produced by this process can store one bit of information. Typical cores are about one-twentieth of an inch in diameter; twice as large as the period at the end of this sentence. Hundreds of thousands (or even millions) of cores are used in the average computer memory. Some of the advantages that ferrite core

memories offer are random access, high operating speed, exceptional reliability, moderately large capacity and a reasonably low cost per bit.

Before discussing complete ferrite core memory systems let's consider the
operation of a single core. A ferrite core is a bistable device: it may be
magnetized in either of two directions, clockwise or counter-clockwise,
each direction representing a stable state. It is magnetized by the magnetic
field surrounding a current-carrying wire which threads the core. As shown
in Fig. 8-9, the direction of magnetization depends on the direction of
current flow in the wire.

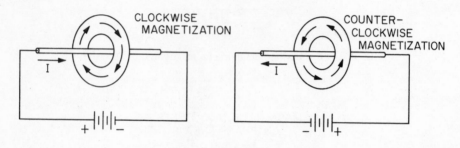

FIG. 8-9.

We will denote the clockwise direction as the 1 state, and the counter-
clockwise direction as the 0 state. Thus, a positive current sets the core in
the 1 state, while a negative current resets the core to 0.

Ferrite cores possess high *retentivity*. This means that the core pictured
in Fig. 8-9 will retain much of its magnetization after the current flow
through the wire is interrupted. The direction of residual magnetization, or
remanence (in other words, the state of the core) depends on the polarity
of the current flow just prior to interruption.

Suppose that a ferrite core is in the 1 state (clockwise direction of magnetic flux) and no current is flowing through the winding (we will refer to
all wires threading the core as windings even though they only pass through
the center once and aren't really wound around the core). Suppose, further,
that we wish to switch the core to the 0 state. Causing this change of states
seems simple enough: just pass a negative pulse of current through the
winding. If we experimented, though, we would soon find that the core
did not switch states unless the amplitude of the current pulse was greater
than some minimum value.

Since the magnetizing force of the magnetic field surrounding the winding
is proportional to the current amplitude, our experiment shows that the
magnetizing force must be greater than some minimum value if it is to
overcome the remanence of the core and change the direction of magnetization. We will label the magnitude of the absolute minimum magnetizing

force necessary to switch the core state H_o, and the current that causes it (an absolute minimum amplitude) I_o.

The relationship between the magnetic flux in the core, denoted by the symbol B, and the magnetizing force H can be shown graphically by plotting B against H. The resulting curve is called a *hysteresis loop* (Fig. 8-10).

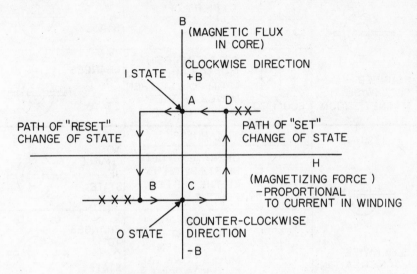

FIG. 8-10.   The hysteresis loop for an ideal ferrite core.

The conditions given above placed the core in the 1 state, with winding current equal to zero (no magnetizing force). These conditions are met at point A on the hysteresis loop. If the magnetizing force H is made equal to $-H_o$ by passing a current pulse of amplitude $-I_o$ through the winding, the core will switch states. The operating point, as indicated on the B-H plot, first moves left along the curve, then down to point B during the pulse, and then to point C at the end of the pulse. Point C meets the conditions where the core is in the 0 state and the magnetizing force is zero (no current flowing in the winding).

If, on the other hand, a current pulse of lesser amplitude is passed through the winding, the operating point will move to the left, but not far enough to "go over the edge" to point B. Instead, at the completion of the pulse, the operating point will return to point A; the core will not change states.

In the same way, a positive current pulse of amplitude $+I_o$, or greater, is required to switch the core from the 0 to the 1 state. On the B-H plot this is pictured as a shift of the operating point from point C to point D during the pulse, and then to point A at the end of the pulse.

The single winding described above enabled us to read-in information to the core. We could set the core to 1 and reset it to 0. A second, identical

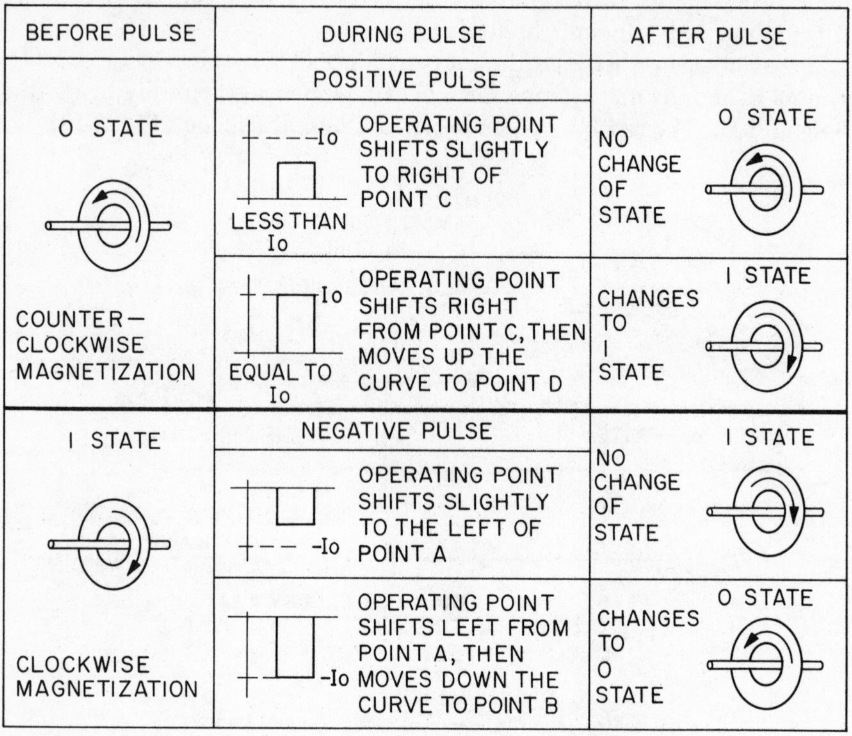

BEFORE PULSE	DURING PULSE		AFTER PULSE
O STATE	POSITIVE PULSE		
	LESS THAN I_0	OPERATING POINT SHIFTS SLIGHTLY TO RIGHT OF POINT C	NO CHANGE OF STATE — O STATE
COUNTER-CLOCKWISE MAGNETIZATION	EQUAL TO I_0	OPERATING POINT SHIFTS RIGHT FROM POINT C, THEN MOVES UP THE CURVE TO POINT D	CHANGES TO I STATE — I STATE
I STATE	NEGATIVE PULSE		
		OPERATING POINT SHIFTS SLIGHTLY TO THE LEFT OF POINT A	NO CHANGE OF STATE — I STATE
CLOCKWISE MAGNETIZATION		OPERATING POINT SHIFTS LEFT FROM POINT A, THEN MOVES DOWN THE CURVE TO POINT B	CHANGES TO O STATE — O STATE

Fig. 8-11.

winding threading the core will allow us to read-out the stored bit of information. The read-out technique is based on the fact that when the core changes its state, the resulting rapid reversal of magnetic field direction will induce a sizeable current pulse in the output winding. To read-out the core we apply a $-I_0$ amplitude current pulse to the input winding (in other words, read-in 0) while watching the output winding. If we observe an output pulse we know the core has changed. Thus, the core was storing a 1. If there is little or no output signal we assume that the core did not change state, and hence was storing a 0. The major difficulty with this read-out scheme is that it is *destructive;* reading-out the stored bit destroys it, or erases it from memory. (Contrast this with magnetic tape or disc memories!) To circumvent this problem, core memories are equipped with auxiliary circuits that temporarily remember the contents of the cores before read-out, and feed the correct states back into the cores after the read-out step.

Memory circuitry would become prohibitively complex if individual input and output windings were run to each of the hundreds of thousands of cores

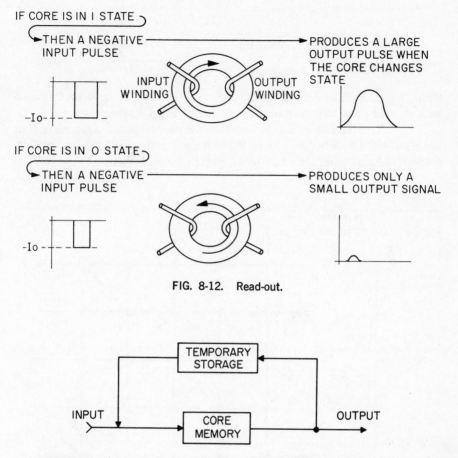

FIG. 8-12. Read-out.

FIG. 8-13. Restoring the contents of a core memory after destructive readout.

in the memory. Instead, a large number of cores are mounted in a two-dimensional array called a *matrix* or *core plane*. To illustrate, a five-by-five matrix containing 25 cores is pictured in Fig. 8-14. Actual memory matrices are many times larger. Notice that each core is threaded by three windings: one of the five X wires; one of the five Y wires; and a single output or *sense* winding passing through all 25 cores.

With the aid of the *coincident current selection technique* it is possible to read-in or read-out from any specified core. Suppose we desire to read-in 1 to core X_2Y_3 (the core at the intersection of the X_2 lead and Y_3 lead). We simultaneously pass current of $+I_o/2$ amplitude through windings X_2 and Y_3. Since both of these windings pass through the specified core, the *total current pulse* threading the core has amplitude:

From X_2 winding	$+\dfrac{I_o}{2}$
From Y_3 winding	$+\dfrac{I_o}{2}$
Total amplitude	$+ I_o$

Thus, 1 is read-in to core X_2Y_3, the only core in the matrix to be threaded by a current pulse sufficient to cause a change in its magnetic state.

Core X_2Y_3 is known as the *fully-selected* core; the other eight cores that are threaded by either winding X_2 or Y_3 are *half-selected* cores, since a current pulse of amplitude $I_o/2$, only, passed through them.

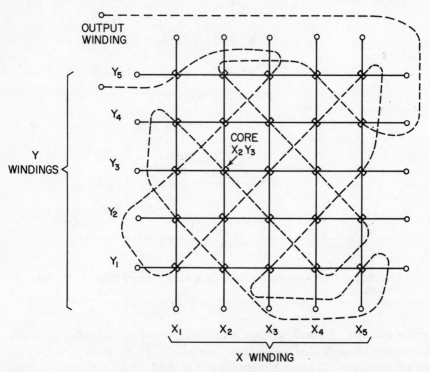

FIG. 8-14.   A five-by-five core matrix.

Read-out of a specific core in the matrix is performed in much the same manner as the read-out of a single core described above. A 0 is read-in to the selected core by passing currents of amplitude $-I_o/2$ through the appropriate X and Y leads, and observing the presence or absence of a signal on the output winding. Since only one core in the matrix can possibly change state during read-out (the full-selected core), it is necessary to have only one continuous output winding passing through every core on the matrix. If a pulse appears on the output winding there is no doubt where it came from!

A ferrite core memory system capable of storing complete words can be assembled by stacking several two-dimensional matrices; the number of matrices usually equaling the number of bits of the word length. Suppose we require a memory that can store words ten bits long. By stacking ten of the five-by-five matrices described above we could build a memory having a capacity of 25 words. The first matrix stores all of the 2^0 bits (the first bits of all 25 words); the second matrix stores the 2^1 bits; the third matrix the 2^2 bits; and so on.

This assignment of storage postions enables us to interconnect the corresponding X and Y leads of the matrices in series, and bring out a single set of X and Y leads. If we pass an $I_o/2$ amplitude current pulse through the X_2 and Y_3 leads, the pulse flows through the X_2 and Y_3 windings of every matrix in the stack. Thus, we full-select the 10 X_2Y_3 cores in the stack simultaneously, which is another way of saying that we select the full word X_2Y_3. Actually, the ten X_2Y_3 cores together make up one of the 25 addresses or locations in the memory.

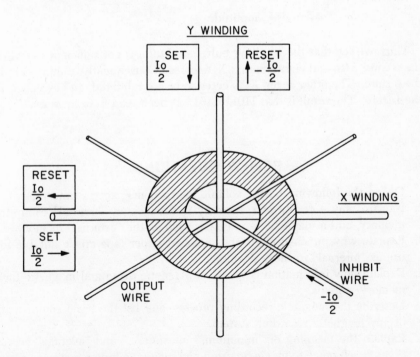

FIG. 8-15.   A single ferrite core showing the four wires that thread it and the direction of current flow involved in the different operations.

One problem arises, though. During the read-in, full-select of all 10 cores simultaneously means that all the cores will be set to 1. (We may assume that the cores have been cleared, or reset to 0, before the read-in operation.) The answer to this problem is a fourth winding on each matrix which passes through every core, similar to the output lead. This winding is usually termed the *inhibit* winding. Its function is obvious from its name; it inhibits the storage of a 1. Suppose that we wanted to write the word 1101101101 into location X_2Y_3. As described above, we would full-select the 10 X_2Y_3 cores simultaneously; *but*, at the same time, we would pass a $-I_o/2$ amplitude current pulse (negative pulse) through the second, fifth and eighth matrix inhibit windings. Such an action would produce a current threading the X_2Y_3 cores in these three matrices of the following amplitude:

From X_2 winding	$+\dfrac{I_o}{2}$
From Y_3 winding	$+\dfrac{I_o}{2}$
From inhibit winding	$-\dfrac{I_o}{2}$
Total pulse amplitude	$+\dfrac{I_o}{2}$

Thus, we see that the resulting pulse amplitude is not sufficient to switch the second, fifth and eighth matrix X_2Y_3 cores. Consequently, they remain in the 0 state. The other seven X_2Y_3 cores were not inhibited, and switched to the 1 state. The result is that 1101101101 has been read-in to memory.

REVIEW QUESTIONS

1. Define the following terms: volatile, permanence, access time.
2. Explain why a ferrite core memory is used as an "internal" computer memory, and a magnetic tape unit is used as the "external" memory.
3. Explain why punched cards and punched paper tape aren't suitable for use as "internal" memory devices.
4. Explain how information is stored in magnetic drum and magnetic tape memory systems.
5. Describe the magnetic recording process, and list the basic components of any magnetic recording system.
6. Explain the meaning of "minimum," "maximum," and "average" access times in reference to magnetic drum and magnetic tape memory systems.
7. Explain the process by which a ferrite core stores a binary digit. Explain the meaning of "destructive read-out."

8. Describe a ferrite core memory system that can store 4000 twenty-bit words. How many memory planes must it have? How many cores does each plane contain?

9. Contrast the memory systems described in this chapter in regard to their size, complexity, type of access, estimated cost per bit (high, medium, low etc.), capacity and access time.

Appendices

Appendix 1: *HINTS FOR FINDING CIRCUIT DIAGRAMS FROM EQUATIONS*

1. The number of AND operation symbols, "·", equals the number of AND gates in the circuit.
2. The number of OR operation symbols, "+", equals the number of OR gates in the circuit.
3. The number of complement (inverse) operation symbols in an equation equals the number of inverters in the circuit. For example:

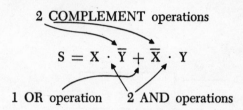

2 COMPLEMENT operations

$$S = X \cdot \overline{Y} + \overline{X} \cdot Y$$

1 OR operation   2 AND operations

Therefore, there are 2 AND gates, 1 OR gate and 2 inverters.

Appendix 2: *SCHEMATIC SYMBOLS*

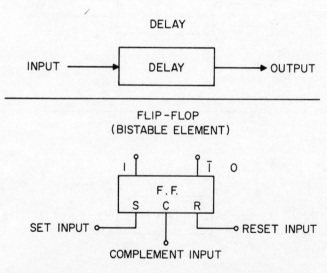

DELAY

INPUT ⟶ DELAY ⟶ OUTPUT

FLIP-FLOP
(BISTABLE ELEMENT)

1    $\overline{1}$ 0

F. F.
S   C   R

SET INPUT ⟶   ⟶ RESET INPUT

COMPLEMENT INPUT

NOTE: IF ONE OR MORE TERMINALS ARE NOT USED IN A SPECIFIC APPLICATION, THE CORRESPONDING LEADS WILL NOT BE SHOWN IN THE CIRCUIT DIAGRAM.

ELECTRICAL SIGNALS

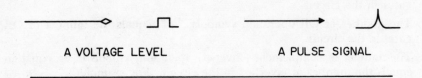

A VOLTAGE LEVEL   A PULSE SIGNAL

GATES

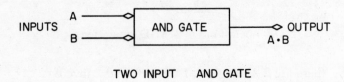

TWO INPUT   AND GATE

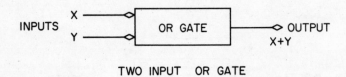

TWO INPUT   OR GATE

INVERTER

Appendix 3: *GLOSSARY OF DIGITAL COMPUTER TERMS*

A

ABACUS. A primitive but very effective calculating machine consisting of wooden beads strung on rods supported by a wooden framework. Each rod of beads represents one of the columns (units, tens, hundreds, etc.) of a decimal number. By manipulating the beads an experienced operator can add, subtract, multiply and divide faster than a worker using a desk calculating machine.

ACCESS TIME. The length of time required to remove a word from a specified memory location, or the length of time required to put a word into a specified memory location. (*See* Random access, Minimum access time, Maximum access time, Average access time.)

ACCUMULATOR. The circuitry found in the arithmetic section that accumulates or totals numbers fed to it. The contents of an accumulator at any time is the sum of all the numbers that have fed into it up to that time. (*See* Accumulator register.)

ACCUMULATOR REGISTER. The register contained in the accumulator that stores the running total of numbers being accumulated.

ADD COMMAND PULSE. An electrical pulse that is applied to appropriate circuitry in the arithmetic section to cause the addition of two numbers.

ADDER. A general term meaning a circuit capable of forming the sum of two or more numbers. (*See* Full adder, Half adder.)

ADDRESS. A number that identifies one of the cells or memory locations in the memory section. Each location has its own address.

ANALOG COMPUTER. An automatic electronic computer that represents quantity with physical variables such as voltage and current. The circuitry is set up as a model or representation of the equation that is being solved.

AND GATE. A gate circuit that performs the logical AND operation. The output will be a signal representing 1, only if all the input signals represent 1. These properties can be described by an input-output relationship table. Such a table for a two input AND gate is shown below:

INPUTS		OUTPUT
X	Y	
0	0	0
1	0	0
0	1	0
1	1	1

ARITHMETIC OPERATION. One of the four basic operations: addition, subtraction, multiplication or division.

ARITHMETIC SECTION. The functional unit of a digital computer that performs the arithmetic operations required to solve a problem.

ASYNCHRONOUS COMPUTER. A digital computer in which the length of the machine cycle depends on the arithmetic operation being performed.

AUTOMATIC COMPUTER. A computer that operates without human control after receiving a program of instructions.

AVERAGE ACCESS TIME. The access time, on the average, of a sequential memory. The arithmetic average of the minimum and maximum access times.

B

BASE. (Radix) The number of different digits used to form numbers in a number system. The octal number system is written to the base 8, and has eight digits: 0, 1, 2, 3, 4, 5, 6 and 7; the decimal number system is written to the base 10, and has ten digits: 0, 1, 2, 3, 4, 5, 6, 7, 8 and 9.

BINARY CODED DECIMAL NUMBERS. A system of writing decimal numbers in binary coded form wherein each decimal digit is represented by a binary number. For example, the decimal number 256 is written in binary coded form as 0010-0101-0110; the decimal 908 is written as 1001-0000-1000.

BINARY DIGIT. One of the two digits in the binary number system. The two digits are usually symbolized by 1 and 0. In two-state electronic circuitry the digits may be represented by "on" and "off;" "high voltage level" and "low voltage level;" "presence of pulse" and "absence of pulse," etc.

BINARY NUMBER. A number written in the binary number system.

BINARY NUMBER SYSTEM. The number system written in the base 2. There are two digits: 0 and 1. The first ten binary numbers and their decimal number equivalents are:

Binary	Decimal	Binary	Decimal
0	0	110	6
1	1	111	7
10	2	1000	8
11	3	1001	9
100	4	1010	10
101	5		

As the above list shows, each digit in a binary number refers to a power of 2. For example, binary 1010 means:

$$1 \times (2^3) + 0 \times (2^2) + 1 \times (2^1) + 0 \times (2^0)$$
$$= 1 \times 8 \quad + 0 \times 4 \quad + 1 \times 2 \quad + 0 \times 1$$
$$= \text{decimal } 10$$

BINARY POINT. The point that separates positive and negative powers of 2 in binary numbers.

BISTABLE CIRCUIT. One of the five basic building blocks. A circuit having two stable states or operating conditions. Used to store binary digits within the calculating and control circuitry, one state represents 1 and the other represents 0.

BISTABLE MULTIVIBRATOR. (*See* Multivibrator.)

BIT. A contraction of BInary digiT. The smallest piece of information flowing within a digital computer.

BOOLEAN ALGEBRA. An algebra capable of representing switching and computer circuitry with mathematical expressions that allows such circuits to be derived "on paper." The constants and variables in Boolean algebraic equations can have only the values 0 or 1.

BRANCH INSTRUCTION. (*See* Jump Instruction.)

BUILDING BLOCK. One of the five basic circuits found in the calculating and control circuity of a digital computer. There are five building blocks: AND gate, OR gate, Inverter (or NOT gate), Bistable circuit and Delay. These five basic circuits, or building blocks, are combined in various arrangements to build the calculating and control circuits.

BUFFER REGISTER. A register that temporarily holds information that has been removed from the memory section until it is transferred to another part of the computer.

C

CAPACITY. The number of bits, or the number of words, that can be stored in a memory device. Also, capacity sometimes refers to the maximum word length a computer can handle.

CAPSTAN. The rotating shaft in a magnetic tape recorder that pulls the tape past the record and playback heads. The capstan rotates at constant speed so that the tape always moves past the heads with a uniform velocity.

CARD PUNCH. A mechanical device used to punch paper cards.

CARD, PUNCHED PAPER. (*See* Punched card.)

CARD READER. A mechanical or photoelectric device used to read the pattern of holes on a punched paper card in order to reclaim the information the card contains.

CARRY-OVER. One of the two digits produced when two digits are added together (in any positional notation number system.) The other digit is called the *sum*. For example, in the binary number system when 1 and 1 are added, the sum digit equals 0 and the carry-over digit equals 1.

CELL. One of the locations in the memory section. Each cell has its own address and can store one complete word.

CHARACTER. A symbol used to represent one of the digits in a number system or one of the letters in the alphabet. In computer terminology, a character sometimes refers to the binary code used to represent a digit or a letter.

CHECK, BUILT-IN. Most computers have the capability to check the operations they perform, such as transferring data between two registers, or arithmetically manipulating two numbers. A check is automatically performed after each operation to determine if an error has been made. If the check indicates an error, the computer will automatically stop.

CLEAR-REGISTER. Setting the numerical contents of a register to zero. In other words, setting each of the bistable elements making up the register to the RESET or 0 state.

CODE. The set of binary numbers that represent the various computer operations. The control section will respond to a properly coded instruction and cause the arithmetic circuitry to perform the called-for operation. A code is often referred to as a "machine language."

CODED DECIMAL NUMBERS, BINARY. (See Binary coded decimal numbers.)
CODE NUMBER, OPERATION. (See Operation code number.)

COLUMN. Each place or position of a positional notation system number. The digit in each column refers to a power of the base number system. For example, the binary number 1101 has four columns; the right-most (or first) referring to 2^0; the second to 2^1; the third to 2^2, and the fourth (or left-most) to 2^3.

COMMAND GENERATOR. A network of AND gates that routes timing pulses throughout the arithmetic section of a computer to activate appropriate circuitry in order to carry out the command called for in the instruction being performed. The command generator actually consists of several sections, one for each operation the computer can perform. Each section is connected to one of the outputs of the *operation decoding matrix*. As soon as an instruction is decoded by the decoding matrix, the corresponding section of the command generator is set into operation. The output of the command generator is a series of properly timed *command pulses*.

COMMAND PULSE. An electrical pulse capable of activating arithmetic and control circuitry.

COMPLEMENT. In the binary number system, the number formed by replacing all the 1's in a binary number by 0's, and all the 0's by 1's. For example, the complement of 101010 is 010101; the complement of 111000111 is 000111000.

COMPUTER. A machine that operates on input numbers to produce output numbers. The input numbers may be problem data and output numbers an answer, or the input numbers may be raw information and the output numbers processed information.

COMPUTER, ANALOG. (See Analog computer.)
COMPUTER, ASYNCHRONOUS. (See Asynchronous computer.)
COMPUTER, AUTOMATIC. (See Automatic computer.)
COMPUTER, DIGITAL. (See Digital computer.)
COMPUTER, SYNCHRONOUS. (See Synchronous computer.)
CONDITIONAL INSTRUCTION. (See Jump instruction.)
CONTENTS. The information, in numerical form, held within a register.

CONTROL CIRCUITRY. The circuitry in a digital computer that interprets the program of instructions and causes the called-for operations to be performed.

CONTROL SECTION. One of the five functional sections of a digital computer. The general term that describes all of the control circuitry, which is usually spread throughout a computer.

CONVERT. To transform a number written in one number system into its equivalent, expressed in another number system. For example, decimal 25 can be converted into the following equivalent numbers: Octal 31 ; Quinary 50 ; Binary 11001.

CORE, MAGNETIC. (*See* Ferrite core.)

COUNTER. In computer terminology, a device that counts the number of electrical pulses applied to its input terminal. A decimal counter displays the count in decimal notation, while a binary counter indicates the count in binary notation.

COUNTER, RING. (*See* Ring counter.)
CYCLE, MACHINE. (*See* Machine cycle.)

D

DATA. Any information fed into a computer that will be used during the operation of the computer. Most often, data consists of problem numbers, such as the given value of constants, for the problem being solved.

DECIMAL POINT. The point that separates positive and negative powers of 10 in decimal numbers.

DECIMAL-TO-BINARY CONVERSION. The process of converting a decimal (base 10) number to its binary number system (base 2) equivalent.

DECODE. To interpret an instruction in order to determine which computer operation has been called for. (*See* Instruction, Command generator, Operation decoding matrix.)

DECODING MATRIX. (*See* Operation decoding matrix.)

DELAY. One of the five basic digital computer building blocks. A delay has an input and an output. The output signal resembles the input signal except that it is produced some short fixed time after the input signal has been applied. Delays are used to "slow" the movement of electrical signals within the calculating and control circuitry. (*See* Delay line, electric and Delay line, electro-acoustic.)

DELAY LINE, ELECTRIC. Basically, a long length of coaxial cable. A signal applied to one end must travel through the cable before appearing at the other end. Thus, the line delays the signals for a short fixed length of time which depends on the length of the cable and the speed of the signal travel-·ing along the cable.

DELAY LINE, ELECTRO-ACOUSTIC. A device consisting of three parts: an input transducer, a sound conducting medium, and an output transducer. An input signal is converted to a sound pulse by the input transducer. The sound pulse travels through the conducting medium at the speed of sound until it strikes the output transducer, which converts it back to an electrical signal. The transducers are usually made of quartz; the sound conducting medium is either mercury or quartz.

DESIGN, LOGICAL. (*See* Logical design.)

DIGIT. One of the n whole numbers, ranging from 0 to $(n-1)$, used to represent quantity in a number system written to the base n. For example, the decimal number system (base 10) has ten digits: 0, 1, 2, 3, 4, 5, 6, 7, 8 and 9; the binary number system (base 2) has two digits: 0 and 1.

DIGITAL. A term used to describe a calculating mechanism that uses integers to represent quantity.

DIGITAL COMPUTER. A computer that uses integers to represent quantity. In effect, digital computers perform arithmetic using numbers in much the same way as a person does arithmetic with "pencil and paper," "by hand."

DRUM, MAGNETIC. (*See* Magnetic drum.)

E

ECCLES-JORDAN CIRCUIT. (*See* Multivibrator.)

ERASE. To clear, or set to 0, all of the bit storage locations of a memory device. The term usually refers only to magnetic memory devices such as magnetic tape memories and magnetic drum memories.

EXECUTE. To perform the operation called for by an instruction.

F

FERRITE CORE. A small toroidal (donut-shaped) piece of ceramic-like ferro-magnetic material. The core can be magnetized in one of two directions (clockwise or counterclockwise) by a pulse of current flowing through a wire passing through the center of the core. Current of one polarity magnetizes the core in the clockwise direction; current of the other polarity magnetizes the core in the counterclockwise direction. The core retains the direction of magnetization caused by a pulse. Thus, a ferrite core can be used as a bistable device capable of storing a binary digit. One direction of magnetization represents 0 and the other direction represents 1. The core can be set to either value by passing a current pulse of appropriate polarity through the wire threading the center of the core.

FERRITE CORE MEMORY. A memory device built of arrays of ferrite cores. Each core can store a single bit. The cores are usually arranged in memory planes; each memory plane storing the corresponding digits of all the words stored in memory. Thus, a memory built to store 10-bit words would have ten memory planes. If each memory plane had one hundred cores, the total storage capacity would be one hundred 10-bit words.

FLIP-FLOP. (*See* Multivibrator.)

FLOW DIAGRAM. A pictorial representation of the sequence of simple arith-metic operations necessary to solve a problem.

FULL ADDER. An adder circuit that may be used in an adding device that will add the contents of two registers. Since every corresponding pair of digits of the two binary numbers are added individually, each adder circuit must have three inputs: an addend bit input, X; an augend bit input, Y; and a carry-in bit input, C_i. The carry-in bit is actually the carry-over bit generated when the preceding pair of digits is added. The full adder has two outputs: a sum bit output, S; and a carry-over bit output, C_o, which is applied to the next adder stage. The input-output relationship table of the full adder is:

INPUTS			OUTPUTS	
C_i	X	Y	S	C_o
0	0	0	0	0
0	0	1	1	0
0	1	0	1	0
0	1	1	0	1
1	0	0	1	0
1	0	1	0	1
1	1	0	0	1
1	1	1	1	1

FUNCTIONAL SECTION. A digital computer can be thought of as being made up of five "black boxes," each performing a certain function. In this text, these black boxes have been called functional sections. The five sections are the *Input section, Output section, Arithmetic section, Control section* and *Memory section.*

G

GATE. A circuit that performs one of the logical operations. The output will be a 1 bit only if the input bits are of correct value. An *AND gate* generates a 1 bit only if all of the input bits equal 1. An *OR gate* generates a 1 bit if any of the input bits equals 1.

H

HALF ADDER. A circuit capable of adding together two binary digits. The half adder has two inputs: an addend bit, X, and an augend bit, Y; and two outputs: a sum bit, S, and a carry-over bit, C_o. The input-output relationship table for the half adder is as follows:

INPUTS		OUTPUTS	
X	Y	C_o	S
0	0	0	0
1	0	0	1
0	1	0	1
1	1	1	0

HEAD, MAGNETIC. (See Magnetic head.)

HYSTERESIS LOOP. A square-shaped curve that shows the magnetization properties of a ferrite core.

I

INFORMATION. The binary numbers flowing within a digital computer. Information includes numerically coded instructions, problem numbers and intermediate results flowing among the five functional sections.

INPUT-OUTPUT RELATIONSHIP TABLE. A table that describes the properties of a logical circuit. All possible combinations of input variables are listed along with the output(s) that each combination produces.

INPUT SECTION. The circuitry and equipment used to feed information into a digital computer. At the start of a "run" the programmer feeds instructions and problem numbers into the input section.

INSTRUCTION. A numerically coded command, in machine language, that orders the computer to perform some operation. An instruction is made up of two parts: an *operation code number* and an *operation data address*.

INSTRUCTION REGISTER. A register that holds an instruction while it is being followed. At the start of each machine cycle, an instruction is withdrawn from the memory section and placed in the instruction register.

INTERMEDIATE RESULTS. The results of the individual steps that make up the long sequence of steps required to solve a problem. Often, intermediate results will be temporarily stored in the memory section for later use.

INTERNAL MEMORY. A moderate capacity, short access time, random access memory contained within a digital computer. In contrast, an external memory is usually a large capacity, sequential access memory device that serves as a "reference library." The internal memory performs the functions associated with the *memory section*.

J

JUMP INSTRUCTION. An instruction that tells the computer to disregard the prescribed sequence of instructions in the memory section, and instead take the next instruction from the memory location specified in the jump instruction's operation data address. There are two kinds of jump instructions: a non-conditional jump instruction causes the computer to "jump" to the specified memory location as soon as it is decoded. The conditional jump instruction causes the computer to jump to the specified location only if certain conditions exist. The "jump if minus" instruction, for example, commands that the computer jump only if the number in the accumulator is negative.

L

LANGUAGE. (*See* Code.)

LOGIC. The branch of philosophy that studies the human thinking and reasoning processes, and investigates the validity of conclusions reached.

LOGICAL DESIGN. The overall plan of a digital computer, organized not in terms of electronic components but rather as an arrangement of the five basic building blocks, used over and over again.

LOGIC LEVELS. The two voltage levels used to represent 0 and 1 within the calculating and control circuitry of a computer. Often, several different sets of logic levels are used in a single computer.

M

MACHINE CYCLE. The length of time required to obey one instruction. The following operations are performed during a single machine cycle: an instruction is withdrawn from the memory section; the instruction is interpreted; the called-for arithmetic operation is carried out.

MACHINE LANGUAGE. (See Code.)

MAGNETIC DRUM. A magnetic recording storage device consisting of an aluminum cylinder (or drum) covered with a thin layer of iron oxide. Information is stored in a series of parallel tracks on the surface of the drum. In operation, the drum is rotated past an array of magnetic heads.

MAGNETIC HEADS. A device used to record (write-in) or play back (readout) information on a magnetic recording surface. The magnetic head consists of a small metal ring with a very narrow gap cut in it. It is energized by means of a coil wrapped around it.

MAGNETIC RECORDING SURFACE. A thin multilayer sandwich of a non-magnetic base material, a thin coating of iron oxide and a protective topcoating. Information is stored on the surface in the form of a pattern of varying surface magnetization directions. One direction represents 0, and the other represents 1. In operation, the surface is drawn past a magnetic recording head. Varying currents passed through the coil wrapped around the head cause the varying surface magnetization.

MAGNETIC TAPE MEMORY. A storage device often used as an external memory. The magnetic tape memory is very similar in operation to a home tape recorder, although it is capable of almost instantaneous starts, stops and changes of direction, and operates at a much higher speed.

MAXIMUM ACCESS TIME. In memory systems having varying access times, the largest possible access time. For example, in a magnetic tape memory the maximum access time is the time required to go from one end of a reel of tape to the other end.

MEMORY SECTION. One of the five functional sections of a digital computer. The memory section stores the program of instruction, problem numbers and intermediate results until they are needed.

MINIMUM ACCESS TIME. The minimum possible time required to gain access to a memory location of a sequential access memory system. Usually, minimum access time is close to zero.

MULTIVIBRATOR. A two-stage amplifier having positive feedback — the output of the first stage is connected to the input of the second, and the output of the second is connected to the input of the first. Depending on the coupling networks used to connect the stages together, a multivibrator can be bistable (two stable states); monostable (one stable state); and astable (no stable states — it oscillates). The bistable multivibrator is known as the Eccles-Jordan circuit (after its inventors) or the flip-flop. The flip-flop is the most common bistable circuit found in electronic digital computers. One stable state represents 1, and the other represents 0. The voltage levels at two output terminals indicate which state the flip-flop is in. Usually, if the flip-flop contains 1, it is said to be in the SET state; if it contains 0, it is said to be in the RESET state. Flip-flops have three input terminals: a SET input, used to set the flip-flop to the SET, or 1, state; a RESET input, used to set the flip-flop to the RESET, or 0, state; and a COMPLEMENT input, used to complement the bit stored in the flip-flop. The monostable multivibrator is often used as a delay circuit. An input pulse will temporarily trigger the circuit out of its single stable state into an unstable operating condition. After a short length of time the circuit will return to its stable operating state. As it does, an output pulse is generated. Thus, the output pulse appears some time after the input pulse — it has been delayed.

N

NOR GATE. A logical building block circuit that can be used either as an AND gate or as an OR gate, depending on the logic levels used to represent 0 and 1.

NUMBER SYSTEM. A set of symbols and associated rules used to represent quantity. (*See* Base, Binary number system.)

O

OPERATION, ARITHMETIC. (*See* Arithmetic operation.)

OPERATION CODE NUMBER. That part of an instruction word that specifies the operation to be performed. A different operation code number is assigned to each of the operations a computer is capable of performing. The code number is decoded by the *operation decoding matrix*, which then controls the *command generator*, causing a chain of *command pulses* to be sent to the appropriate calculating circuits which will carry out the called-for operation.

OPERATION DATA ADDRESS. The part of an instruction word that tells the computer the memory location of the number word to be used in the called-for operation.

OPERATION DECODING MATRIX. A network of AND gates that decodes the instruction code number of each instruction. The decoding matrix has one output for each of the operations the computer is capable of performing. An output signal will be produced only at the output terminal corresponding to the operation called for by the operation code number.

OR GATE. A gate circuit that performs the logical OR operation. The output will be a signal representing 1 if any of the input signals represents 1.

These properties can be described by an input-output relationship table. Such a table for a two-input OR gate is shown below:

INPUTS		OUTPUT
X	Y	
0	0	0
1	0	1
0	1	1
1	1	1

OUTPUT SECTION. One of the five basic functional *sections*. The circuitry and equipment used to transfer processed information and answers out of a digital computer. At the end of a "run" the final results are displayed by the output section.

P

PARALLEL OPERATION. Computer operation in which all the bits of a word or words are handled simultaneously, by separate, identical circuits. In parallel transfer techniques, each bit of a word is transmitted over a separate wire. In parallel addition, each pair of corresponding digits of the two numbers being added are summed simultaneously. Parallel operation contrasts with *serial operation*.

PROGRAM. The set of step-by-step instructions fed into a digital computer in order to solve a problem.

PROGRAM COUNTER. A binary counter located in the control section that keeps track of the address of the next instruction to be performed.

PROGRAMMER. The person who formulates the program of instructions.

PUNCHED CARD. A rectangular card used as an input device and for large capacity external memories. Information is recorded on a punched card in a coded pattern of holes.

PUNCHED PAPER TAPE. Paper tape used as an input device and for large capacity external memories. Information is recorded on the tape in the form of a coded pattern of punched holes.

R

RANDOM ACCESS. The ability of a memory device to "remember" the contents of any memory location immediately. That is, a random access memory system provides immediate access to any one of the memory cells.

READ-OUT. To transfer a word from a memory location to some other register in the computer.

REGISTER. An array of bistable circuits that can store a computer word. Each bistable circuit stores a single bit of the word.

RESET. The state of a flip-flop that represents 0.

RING COUNTER. Three or more flip-flops (or other bistable devices) and associated gate elements interconnected such that only one of the flip-flops is ON (in the 1 state) at any time; series of input pulses will advance the ON state around the ring of flip-flops, one step for each input pulse.

ROUTINE. A set of step-by-step instructions fed to a computer. Similar in meaning to *program*.

RUN. The performance of a program of instructions by a computer.

S

SENSE WINDING. A wire that threads all the ferrite cores in a single memory plane. The sense winding is used to determine the state of the cores, that is, the value of the bits they contain.

SEQUENTIAL ACCESS. A term that describes a memory system that "remembers" the contents of the various memory locations in a sequential, or one after another fashion. Magnetic tape memories are sequential access since reading-out the contents of a location on the tape may require going past several other locations first.

SERIAL OPERATION. Computer operation in which the bits of a word or words are handled individually, in a sequential, one after another fashion, by a single circuit. In serial transfer techniques, the bits of a word are transmitted one at a time over a single wire. In serial addition, each pair of corresponding digits of the two numbers being added are summed one at a time by a single adder circuit. Serial operation contrasts with *parallel operation*.

SET. The state of a flip-flop that represents 1.

STEP. One of the simple operations required to solve a complex problem. Computer solution of a complex problem requires that it be broken up into a sequence of simple steps.

STORAGE. (*See* Memory section.)

STORE. To place a piece of information into a memory device from which it can be "remembered" at some later time.

SUBROUTINE. A part of a larger program. A set of instructions for performing a well-defined mathematical operation.

SYNCHRONOUS COMPUTER. A digital computer in which the "machine cycle" is of constant length, regardless of the arithmetic operation being performed.

T

TAPE, MAGNETIC. (*See* Magnetic tape.)

TIME PULSE DISTRIBUTOR. A circuit that generates a number of timing pulses at uniform intervals during the machine cycle. These time pulses are gated throughout the calculating and control circuitry by the *command generator* and activate the appropriate circuitry to carry out the called-for operation.

TRANSFER. To move information from one location to another. Usually, transfer refers to the process of shifting words from one register to another.

V

VOLATILE. A term used to describe a memory device. The contents of a volatile memory system will be lost if power is removed from the system.

W

WORD. A group of digits handled by a digital computer as a single unit. There are two types of words: instruction words, and problem number words. Instruction words order the computer to perform some operation; problem number words are the values of constants or other numbers that will be used during the calculation.

Appendix 4: *BIBLIOGRAPHY*

1. Semi-technical basic introductory texts:

    Stabitz and Larrivee. *Mathematics and Computers*. New York: McGraw-Hill Book Co., Inc., 1957.

    Eckert and Jones. *Faster, Faster*. New York: McGraw-Hill Book Co., Inc., 1955.

    Both books are for the interested layman rather than the student, and consequently contain much fascinating historical material rarely included in more technical texts.

2. Broad introductory texts:

    Murphy, John S. *Basics of Digital Computers*. New York: John F. Rider Publisher, Inc., 1958.

    Bartee, Thomas C. *Digital Computer Fundamentals*. New York: McGraw-Hill Book Co., Inc., 1960.

    Ledley, Robert S. *Digital Computer and Control Engineering*. New York: McGraw-Hill Book Co., Inc., 1960.

    Huskey and Kohn. *Computer Handbook*. New York: McGraw-Hill Book Co., Inc., 1962.

    Listed in order of increasing complexity and quantity of material discussed, these four texts have one thing in common: broad coverage of digital computer theory and technology. The last one is more a reference volume than a text book.

3. Boolean algebra and switching circuits:

    Whitesitt, J. Eldon. *Boolean Algebra and Its Applications*. Reading, Mass.: Addison-Wesley Publishing Co., Inc., 1961.

    Humphrey, Watts S. *Switching Circuits with Computer Applications*. New York: McGraw-Hill Book Co., Inc., 1958.

    Both texts are straightforward introductions to Boolean algebra and its use in logical design. The first leans more toward formal mathematics and discusses symbolic logic and some basic set theory. The second is aimed at the engineering student, and presents many techniques of switching circuit design.

4. Computer circuitry:

    Millman and Taub. *Pulse and Digital Circuits*. New York: McGraw-Hill Book Co., Inc., 1956.

Pressman, A. I. *Design of Transistorized Circuits for Digital Computers.* New York: John F. Rider Publisher, Inc., 1959.

Pettit, Joseph M. *Electronic Switching, Timing and Pulse Circuits.* New York: McGraw-Hill Book Co., Inc., 1959.

Reich, H. J. *Functional Circuits and Oscillators.* Princeton, N. J.: D. Van Nostrand, 1961.

First on the list is a text devoted almost completely to vacuum tube circuits, while the second is concerned only with transistor circuits. The third and fourth texts are more general, but still contain a good deal of material directly applicable to digital computers.

5. Logical design:

Flores, Ivan. *Computer Logic.* Englewood Cliffs, N. J.: Prentice-Hall, Inc., 1961.

Chu, Yaohan. *Digital Computer Design Fundamentals.* New York: McGraw-Hill Book Co., Inc., 1962.

The first book listed above could fairly have been mentioned above as an introductory text. It's oriented toward logical design but still contains a sizable amount of material on other facets of digital computation. The second book is less general, filling up the saved space with discussion of many of the newest logical circuit elements.

INDEX